The Eternal Form of Cosmos Theory

Third Edition of Fractal Cosmic Curve

Fractal Cosmos Grid
Main Sequence of Cosmos Spaces
Building the Cosmos: Dimension by Dimension
The Reason for Ten Physical HyperCosmos Spaces

Stephen Blaha Ph. D.
Blaha Research

Pingree-Hill Publishing
MMXXIV

Rev. 00/00/01   May 12, 2024

To Margaret

Some Other Books by Stephen Blaha

SuperCivilizations: Civilizations as Superorganisms (McMann-Fisher Publishing, Auburn, NH, 2010)

All the Universe! Faster Than Light Tachyon Quark Starships & Particle Accelerators with the LHC as a Prototype Starship Drive Scientific Edition (Pingree-Hill Publishing, Auburn, NH, 2011).

Unification of God Theory and Unified SuperStandard Model THIRD EDITION (Pingree Hill Publishing, Auburn, NH, 2018).

The Exact QED Calculation of the Fine Structure Constant Implies ALL 4D Universes have the Same Physics/Life Prospects (Pingree Hill Publishing, Auburn, NH, 2019).

Passing Through Nature to Eternity ProtoCosmos, HyperCosmos, Unified SuperStandard Theory (Pingree Hill Publishing, Auburn, NH, 2022).

HyperCosmos Fractionation and Fundamental Reference Frame Based Unification: Particle Inner Space Basis of Parton and Dual Resonance Models (Pingree Hill Publishing, Auburn, NH, 2022).

The Cosmic Panorama: ProtoCosmos, HyperCosmos, Unified SuperStandard Theory (UST) Derivation (Pingree Hill Publishing, Auburn, NH, 2022).

God and and Cosmos Theory (Pingree Hill Publishing, Auburn, NH, 2023).

Newton's Apple is Now The Fermion (Pingree Hill Publishing, Auburn, NH, 2023).

Cosmos Theory: The Sub-Particle Gambol Model (Pingree Hill Publishing, Auburn, NH, 2023).

Cosmos-Universe-Particle-Gambol Theory (Pingree Hill Publishing, Auburn, NH, 2024).

Fractal Cosmos Theory (Pingree Hill Publishing, Auburn, NH, 2024).

Fractal Cosmic Curve: Tensor-Based Cosmos Theory (Pingree Hill Publishing, Auburn, NH, 2024).

Available on Amazon.com, bn.com Amazon.co.uk and other international web sites as well as at better bookstores.

CONTENTS

FIGURES and TABLES

Introduction

This Third Edition provides significant additional support for the success of Cosmos Theory:

1. This edition shows that at dimension $r = 18$ the Casimir force changes from greater than the thermodynamic pressure to less than the thermodynamic pressure OR from contraction to expansion of the Parent universe. Thus $r = 18$ marks the beginning of an acceptable Parent universe since $r < 18$ would give a universe that contracts to a point and thus could not generate child universes. The key scale for universe and space dimension is $2e\pi$. This choice of $r = 18$ as the largest possible Physical HyperCosmos space dimension confirms the choice of 10 Physical HyperCosmos spaces.

2. A mechanism for growing dimensions.

3. More detail on the structure of gamma-matrices in even number dimensions.

4. A deeper view of the quadrupling of gamma-matrices, dimension arrays, tensor numbers, and fractal curve orders as dimensions increase by two.

5. An analysis of the structure of dimension arrays when decomposed into 8 dimension parts. The effect on Internal Symmetries leads to the realization that The Standard Model follows from two 8 dimension parts of the $r = 4$ dimension array.

6. The two dimension unit fractal Cosmos Grid, generated by the Cosmos Curve is dissected into points that correspond to Cosmos Theory spaces and their internal symmetries.

7. We identify the Cosmos Theory spaces within the Cosmos Grid as the Main Sequence of Cosmos Spaces.

8. From a zero dimension point to the two dimension fractal Cosmos Grid to the Main Sequence of Cosmos spaces!

9. A procedure is described that generates additional dimensions for a space, and for the space's point, in the Cosmos Curve's two dimension grid.

10. A generation mechanism is described for dimensions in other contexts such as space-times.

11. A comparison of the UST part of Cosmos Theory with the known distribution of Dark Matter and Energy is shown to be accurate to within a few percent.

12. A discussion of energy requirements based on a vacuum propulsion engine, and the possibility of stellar and inter-universe travel at superluminal speed on uniships.

The book expands on previous topics in the Second Edition, namely:

The derivation of Cosmos Theory (and the Unified SuperStandard Theory) from the consideration of unassailable Mathematical truths is expressed in n-forms, wedge operator products, and independent asymmetric tensors.

Gamma-matrices (both Dirac matrices and higher dimension gamma matrices) are derived from these constructs. Similarly the dimension arrays and the spaces of Cosmos Theory are also derived. Gamma-matrices and dimension arrays are very similar. Cosmos dimension arrays perform the same role for internal symmetries as gamma-matrices do for fermion spin.

Gamma-matrices have an internal structure based on a quadrupling of size as the dimension increases by increments of two. Dimension arrays also have a quadrupling of size as the dimension increases by increments of two.

For these reasons one might describe dimension arrays as the dimension-matrices of Internal Symmetries. Dimension-matrices are an integral part of the structure of Cosmos spaces. The impression of some that Cosmos Theory is merely an aggregate of features without a sufficient cause is removed. It now stands as forming the structure of fundamental fermions as much as gamma-matrices.

The spaces structure of Cosmos Theory is similar to that of the fractal Hilbert curve. An analogous fractal Cosmic Curve is be generated with similar features.

The book presents a concise description of new and known Cosmos Theory feature details. For example the fractal Cosmic Curve supports a unique Language.

The formulation of fundamental Physical theory ranging from Cosmos spaces through the experimentally known Standard Model of Elementary Particles continues. The author's intent in creating the series of books on Cosmos Theory was to provide a coherent introduction to the subject based on a careful consideration of alternatives at each stage of the creation process.

The result is a clear passage from a zero dimension point to spaces, to universes and to a well-structured Cosmos!

1. The Origin and The End of the Cosmos

There have been numerous speculations about the Beginning and End of all things. These speculations assume that a space and time exists that can be used to discuss beginnings and endings. We chose to view this assumption with suspicion. Space and time are constructs based on the changes in substances. Where there is no substance they have no meaning.

We assume substances exist only within universes. Space and time within a universe has a beginning and an end – the lifetime and extent of the universe. It is only possible to discuss a before-time or a region beyond the spatial extent of a universe if the universe exists within a larger universe. Thus we have the possibility of before and after, and in and beyond for a universe—only for "contained" universes.

Two possibilities present themselves: there is an infinite chain of nested universes as some propose OR there are one or more primeval Parent universes within which all "child" universes reside. We chose the latter possibility in our definition of the Cosmos.

In Cosmos Theory we may assume that one ultimate Parent universe exists that we chose to be the seed universe. It has eighteen space-time dimensions. We may then assume "child" universes may exist within it including our own universe.

The parent universe specifies the time and spatial extents for its child universes. There is no question of "before" or "after" for the parent universe. All child universes may have their times and extents set relative to their time and extent within the parent universe.

These observations are based on:

1. There can be no dynamics if there is no time or space.
2. Time and distances only exist for substances (including vacuums containing gravitation.)
3. Measures of absolute motion and location are meaningless outside of universes.

1.1 Cosmos Structure

It is possible to consider the Cosmos as composed of universes with random contents and dynamics. We chose to impose order on the set of universes by assuming universes comply with a consistent, related structure of Cosmos Theory. We determined this Cosmos structure from a consideration of the nature of dimensions and coordinates and related quantities such as integrals over the space and time of substances (entities).

Therefore we view the definition of Cosmos Theory as initially beginning with a specification of the general structure of the set of spaces composing the Cosmos. Then universes may be defined or created through dynamical assumptions or mechanisms. We have chosen an ultimate, single Parent universe – an eighteen space-time dimension universe from which all other universes are descended although other possibilities present themselves.

There is no time before this Parent universe(s) and no time after this universe(s) should it end. Cosmos structure exists for all time and space within the Parent universe. It is eternal in Cosmos Theory. Therefore, previous attempts to generate a Cosmos structure such as ProtoCosmos Theory dynamically are beside the point. There is no dynamics before time and space exists in a Parent universe.

1.2 Lifetime of Cosmos Structure and Parent Universe(s)

Our discussions of Cosmos features in the text are necessarily sequential. The structure and content of Cosmos Theory is "instantaneous." The structure of Cosmos Theory spaces exists at the same instant as the Parent universe(s). (There may be more than one Parent universe. Each such universe would be at the top of a hierarchy of possible subuniverses.) The lifetime of a Parent universe must be viewed as zero since there is no external clock to specify a time. The lifetime of a Parent universe is simultaneous with the lifetime of the (eternal) Cosmos structure. The lifetime of a subuniverse depends on universe dynamics.

Within the Parent universe evolution is possible in a dynamics based on the internal Parent time. Thus subuniverses may be generated dynamically through inter-universe dynamics.

1.3 "Eternal" Nature of Cosmos Structure

We have arrived at an open door: the Nonexistence (Nothingness) of Cosmos Theory's origin and structure. It is eternal since there is no time to measure it. The Cosmos structure is not a substance. It only exists to specify the form of Cosmos spaces.

Subuniverses have substance. They have attributes such as mass, energy, internal coordinate systems, and internal structures.

Substances exist within universes. They generally have finite extent and lifetime. They may be called "mortal."

Cosmos Structure is eternal but not substantial. We have shown that its nature is based directly on Mathematics.

1.4 Is What Creates the Cosmos Universes?

There appear to be several points in Cosmos Theory where a creatorr[1] may act. A creator can define the form of the Cosmos Theory set of spaces. This possibility is mitigated somewhat by the mathematical form from which Cosmos Theory is derived. (See the following chapters.) The form, which we derive, may be the only possible form that is without inconsistencies at some level. It also has the virtue of being directly derived from fundamental Mathematical concepts.

---

[1] We view the creator as an instrumentality that initiates a process.

A creator might be the creator of Parent universes, from which all subuniverses flow. There is the question of whether a creator is required since the structure of Cosmos Theory is defined simultaneously with the Parent universe(s) and would end at the same instant as the Parent universe(s) ends.[2]

Within a subuniverse a creator might act. There is no Physical requirement for such interactions.

1.5 Introduction of Quantum Theory

The correct view of Quantum Theory is to regard it as the result of Quantum Field Theory as this author has stated a number of times previously. The Physics of Quantum Mechanics is derivable from Quantum Field Theory.[3]

Therefore the definition of Lagrangian Quantum Field Theories of Physics leads inexorably to the experimentally known Quantum Phenomena. For example Quantum Electrodynamics is the heart and soul of photons, atoms, and their electromagnetic character and interactions.

On this basis we can view Cosmos Theory as implementing Quantum Theory through its use of Lagrangian Quantum Field Theory. Our work uses conventional quantum field theory and our generalization to PseudoQuantum Theory, which has conventional quantum field theory as a subset.

1.6 Fundamental Prerequisites for Cosmos Theory

The views expressed in this chapter are based on:

1. There can be no time or space or dynamics outside of universes.
2. The structure of Cosmos Theory is not substantial.
3. Cosmos Theory contains an overall design that governs the form of spaces and universes.
4. Universes cannot interact with each other unless they are both within a larger universe.
5. The form of Cosmos Theory is solely based on Mathematical considerations that were presented in earlier books by the author, and will be discussed in more detail later in this book.

---

[2] If there are more than one Parent universe, then all Parent universes have the same Cosmos structure by assumption. Parent universes cannot interact because there is no intervening space and time between them. Parent universes are totally independent of each other. Their sets of subuniverses are also independent of each other for the same reason. Multiple Parents constitute totally separate Cosmos's. We will assume only one Parent universe. If other Cosmos Parents exist would be very similar, if not identical, in structure and general features.
[3] Some theorists like to entertain the concept of an independent Quantum Mechanics based on a set of postulates. This approach is mathematically acceptable. But it is not Physics. It is Applied Mathematics. A basis in Quantum Field Theory is necessary for a consistent theory of Physics.

2. Dimensions, Coordinates, and Antisymmetric Tensors

This chapter establishes the Mathematical framework for the derivation of the structure of Cosmos Theory spaces embodied in space dimension arrays. It begins by considering dimensions and sets of coordinates. The considerations of multiple integrations over the spatial extent of objects lead to n-forms, object orientations, and the asymmetric form of wedge products and antisymmetric tensors.

The goal is to develop the basis of γ-matrices (Dirac γ-matrices and γ-matrices in higher dimensions) and the basis for Cosmos Theory dimension arrays.

2.1 Dimension

The concept of dimension requires clarification. We shall begin the discussion by regarding dimension as an ordered set of integers extending from $-\infty$ to $+\infty$. Each integer in the set is a dimension and may be associated with a set of coordinates.

2.2 Coordinate Systems

The nth dimension corresponds to n coordinates that vary over a range of values. These coordinates may be labeled from 1 to n. For each n there is a coordinate system.

2.3 Integration Elements

In any coordinate system one may consider integrations (summations) over the region occupied by an object. Integrations may be defined using volume and area elements of the form

$$dx_1 dx_2 \ldots dx_k \qquad (2.1)$$

for some value $k \leq n$. The factors in each element, if treated as independent integration elements, are "classical." They commute.

2.4 Orientation of Objects

One may introduce orientation for integration over an object.

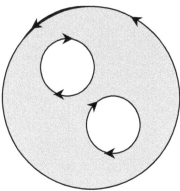

Figure 2.1. An Oriented object.

The object in Fig. 2.1 is shown as oriented. There are rules for orientation specification. One rule states the orientation is specified by "walking around the edge of the object keeping the left hand inside the object." Orientation is usually counterclockwise. Another rule for specifying orientation uses a normal to the object pointing "up" from the object. The orientation of an object enables integrations to embody orientation by the ordering of the factors of the integration element.

2.5 Antisymmetry of Oriented Elements

For example,

$$dxdy = -dydx$$

if the object is oriented. As a result there are oriented differential integration elements which exhibit an antisymmetry. For higher dimension differential elements we obtain totally antisymmetric integration elements.

2.6 n-forms

The totally antisymmetric integration elements lead to totally antisymmetric n-forms. The set of all differential forms for dimension n consists of n + 1 forms that are named 0-form, 1-form, 2-form, ... , n-form. A k-form has k factors corresponding to the differential form $dx_1dx_2 \ldots dx_k$. The 0-form corresponds to an integration with no differential form factor, namely, non-integration.

The k-forms are independent and totally antisymmetric in their factors.

2.7 Structure of n-Forms

If one considers the set of k-forms for a space of dimension n then one sees that may be enumerated due to their antisymmetry.[4] For example if n = 4 we find the following list of antisymmetric k-forms (listed by index):

$$
\begin{array}{lll}
\text{0-form:} & \text{1 item} & - \\
\text{1-form} & \text{4 items} & 1\ 2\ 3\ 4 \\
\text{2-form} & \text{6 items} & 12\ \ 13\ 14\ \ 23\ 24\ 34 \\
\text{3-form} & \text{4 items} & 123\ \ 124\ \ 134\ \ 234 \\
\text{4-form} & \text{1 item} & 1234 \\
\end{array}
$$

The total number of items is $16 = 2^4$ where the power of "4" is the dimension. Note the antisymmetry constrains the set of items for each k-form. Examining the number of items for each k-form above we see they are binomial coefficients:

$$
\begin{bmatrix} r \\ k \end{bmatrix}
$$

---

[44] One may also do enumerations based on other considerations such as, perhaps, totally symmetric tensors. They total to $6^{r/2}$ independent tensors for dimension r. These enumerations are not of interest here.

where r is the dimension of the space. We see r = 4 in the above example.

In general the sum of the (r + 1) k-forms of dimension r

0-form, 1-forms, …. r-form

is[5]

$$2^r \qquad (2.2)$$

2.7.1 Internal Structure of n-Form Distribution

The above example, and the general case, exhibits a regularity. The items of an n-form are a quadruple (suitably arranged) of the (n – 2)-form. For the above n = 4 case we find

n=4   1   4   6   4   1

is the ordered sum of four n-2 forms

```
        1   2   1
            2   4   2          TIMES 2
                1   2   1      TIMES 1
```

TOTAL   1   4   6   4   1

The summation requires offsets of the n-2-form items. We can specify the rule as

$$T_n = T_{n-2} + 2\,T_{n-2}(1) + T_{n-2}(2) \qquad (2.3)$$

where the second and third summand is offset by the number within the parentheses. The total number of n-form elements is

$$2^n \qquad (2.3a)$$

Another summation that generates an n-form combines (n – 1)-forms:

$$T_n = T_{n-1} + T_{n-1}(1) \qquad (2.4)$$

The quadrupling effect carries over to γ-matrices and dimension arrays as we shall see later.

---

[5] In an r dimension space the number of integrand factors for objects: lines, areas, and volume elements must be less then r + 1.

2.8 Wedge Product Representation of n-forms

A k-form may be represented using wedge operators, $\wedge$. Wedge operator expressions are totally antisymmetric. A wedge representation of a k-form is

$$dx_1 dx_2 \ldots dx_k \equiv dx_1 \wedge dx_2 \wedge \ldots \wedge dx_k \qquad (2.5)$$

Wedge expressions satisfy the rules

1. Total antisymmetry. For example

$$dx \wedge dy = - \, dy \wedge dx$$

2. Any wedge product with a pair (multiple) of identical factors is zero. For example

$$dx \wedge dx = 0$$

2.9 Totally Antisymmetric Tensors

The above discussion of n-forms has an equivalent when one considers tensors. The tensors of an r dimension space with indices xyz… have the form:

$$T_{xyz} \ldots$$

Totally antisymmetric tensors have significant Physical applications such as the determination of the form of Dirac γ-matrices in 4 dimensions. Tensor indices range from a zero index tensor through an r index tensor. Thus there are r + 1 types of antisymmetric tensors in r dimensions.

2.10 Number of Independent Antisymmeric Tensors in Even Number Dimensions

The number of independent,[6] totally antisymmetric tensors with k indices in an even r dimension space is the same as the number of items for each k-form seen above. The "number of items" numbers are binomial coefficients:

$$\begin{bmatrix} r \\ k \end{bmatrix}$$

There are r + 1 types of tensors: those tensors with 0 indices, tensors with one index, …, tensors with r indices. The total number of independent antisymmetric tensors obtained by summing the r + 1 binomial coefficients is

$$2^r \qquad (2.6)$$

where r is the dimension of the space.

---

[6] In an odd dimension space tensors are interrelated and as a result the number of independent antisymmetric tensors is 2^{r-1}.

3. Degrees of Freedom of γ-Matrices and Dimension Arrays

The discussion of tensor forms in chapter 2 leads to an understanding of the form of γ-matrices in four and other dimensions. First we note the number of tensors is the same as the number of independent γ-matrices *and* related matrices in dimension r. We only consider the case of even number dimensions.[7]

The number of independent, antisymmetric tensors in even dimension r is given by eq. 2.6. This number is the number of independent components for γ-matrices and related matrices in dimension r. Thus the γ-matrices have 2^r components. Since they are square matrices they have $2^{r/2}$ rows and $2^{r/2}$ columns. For example, Dirac matrices are 4 by 4 matrices in our four dimension space.

3.1 Fermion Spin

We now relate the structure of γ-matrices to the spin of fermions in even number dimension r. The key fact is the number of spins for a dimension is half of the column length of a γ-matrix:

$$\text{Number of spins} = 2^{r/2-1} \qquad (3.1)$$

The lowest spin s of a fermion in dimension r is determined by

$$2s + 1 = \text{Number of spins} = 2^{r/2-1} \qquad (3.2)$$

Therefore the lowest fermion spin in the even dimension r is[8]

$$s = 2^{r/2-2} - \tfrac{1}{2} \qquad (3.3)$$

If r = 4, then s = ½ .

3.2 Fermion Quantum Fields

Having determined the lowest spin of fermions in dimension r we may now turn to the form of fermion quantum fields in that dimension. A Fourier representation

$$\psi(x) = \Sigma_{\alpha,s}[b(\alpha, s)u_{\alpha s}f_\alpha(x) + d^\dagger(\alpha, s)v_{\alpha s}f_\alpha^*(x)] \qquad (3.4)$$

---

[7] As we pointed out previously the odd number dimension cases have the same results as the next lowest even number dimension case. When restricting ourselves to Cosmos Theory, we avoid duplication by considering even number dimensions only.

[8] Those concerned with perturbation theory divergences in higher dimensions are reminded that the Two Tier Theory of the author removes all such divergences for any dimension.

where α represents the Fourier momentum, and s is the spin.

We now enumerate the degrees of freedom that the Fourier coefficients represent. The $2^{r/2-1}$ spins yield $2^{r/2-1}$ b's, which being complex due to $b^\dagger$'s give a total of $2^{r/2}$ real-valued degrees of freedom due to the b's. The d's similarly number $2^{r/2}$. Together there are

$$2^{r/2+1} \text{ real-valued degrees of freedom.} \qquad (3.5)$$

The b's and d's have anticommutation relations that parallel the structure of wedge products described in section 2.8.[9]

Antisymmetry:
$$b(s)b(s') = -b(s')b(s) \qquad (3.6)$$
$$b^\dagger(s)b^\dagger(s') = -b^\dagger(s')b^\dagger(s)$$

$$d(s)d(s') = -d(s')d(s)$$
$$d^\dagger(s)d^\dagger(s') = -d^\dagger(s')d^\dagger(s)$$

$$b(s)d(s') = -d(s')b(s)$$
$$b^\dagger(s)d^\dagger(s') = -d^\dagger(s')b^\dagger(s)$$

Repeated factors are zero: any product of factors containing repeated factors are zero (Pauli) when applied to states

$$b(s)b(s) \equiv 0 \qquad (3.7)$$
$$d(s)d(s) \equiv 0$$
$$b^\dagger(s)b^\dagger(s) \equiv 0$$
$$d^\dagger(s)d^\dagger(s) \equiv 0$$

Thus independent wedge products and *independent* creation/annihilation products have the same antisymmetric algebra.

We now turn to our PseudoQuantum fermions with two fields. We have pointed out their benefits in previous work.

3.3 PseudoQuantum Fermion Fields' Operators

If we consider the form of a fermion's PseudoQuantum fields[10] the number of b's and d's doubles

$$\psi_1(x) = \Sigma_{\alpha,s}[b_1(\alpha, s)u_{\alpha s}f_\alpha(x) + d^\dagger_1(\alpha, s)v_{\alpha s}f_\alpha{}^*(x)] \qquad (3.8)$$
$$\psi_2(x) = \Sigma_{\alpha,s}[b_2(\alpha, s)u_{\alpha s}f_\alpha(x) + d^\dagger_2(\alpha, s)v_{\alpha s}f_\alpha{}^*(x)]$$

---

[9] For Fourier index α. It is understood that the creation and annihilation operators are explicitly or implicitly functions of momentum in this book.
[10] In our PseudoQuantum formulation of fermions in the 1970's and recently we define two wave functions for each fermion for important reasons presented in my earlier papers and books.

where α represents the Fourier momentum, then the total number of creation and annihilation (CAO) operators doubles to

$$d_{cr} = 2^{r/2 + 2} \qquad (3.9)$$

which represent real-valued degrees of freedom.

The column length d_{cr} (used in Cosmos Theory) specifies degrees of freedom since the associated creation and annihilation operators generate independent states.

Note the set of PseudoQuantum type 1 operators b_1's, $b_1{}^\dagger$'s, d_1's, and $d_1{}^\dagger$'s all anticommute just as the independent asymmetric k-forms all anti-commute.

Antisymmetric products of creation and annihilation operators may be formed. Any product with repeated operators is zero when they are applied to the vacuum state. This limits the number of factors in a product to d_{cr} just as the k-forms are limited to have at most r factors in dimension r. Due to the algebraic properties[11] we find that there are

$$2^{R/2+1} = \text{total number of non-zero products of } b_1\text{'s, } b_1{}^\dagger\text{'s, } d_1\text{'s, and } d_1{}^\dagger\text{'s}$$
$$= 2^S \qquad (3.10)$$

where $R = 2^{r/2+1}$ is the number of b_1's, $b_1{}^\dagger$'s, d_1's, and $d_1{}^\dagger$'s, and where $S = 2^{r/2} + 1$ using eq. 3.5.

The above comments also apply directly to the set of PseudoQuantum type 2 b_2's, $b_2{}^\dagger$'s, d_2's, and $d_2{}^\dagger$'s. The resulting total number of degrees of freedom are given by eq. 3.9.

The total number of non-zero products[12] of b_1's, $b_1{}^\dagger$'s, d_1's, $d_1{}^\dagger$'s b_2's, $b_2{}^\dagger$'s, d_2's, and $d_2{}^\dagger$'s – before reducing the set of products using the non-zero anti-commutators $\{b_1, d_2{}^\dagger\}$, $\{b_1{}^\dagger, d_2\}$, $\{b_2, d_1{}^\dagger\}$, $\{b_2{}^\dagger, d_{21}\}$ – is

$$2^{R'/2+1} = 2^{S'} \qquad (3.11)$$

where $R' = 2^{r/2+2}$ is the number of all b's, b†'s, d_1's, and d†'s, and where

$$S' = 2^{r/2 + 1} + 1 \qquad (3.12)$$

3.4 Dimension Arrays and Internal Symmetries

The column length d_{cr} is due to spin counting of a PseudoQuantum fermion. We now make the *ansatz* that there is an equal number of internal symmetry states represented by an index k. Then eq. 3.8 becomes

$$\psi_{1k}(x) = \Sigma_{\alpha,s}[b_{1k}(\alpha, s)u_{\alpha s}f_\alpha(x) + d^\dagger{}_{1k}(\alpha, s)v_{\alpha s}f_\alpha{}^*(x)] \qquad (3.13)$$
$$\psi_{2k}(x) = \Sigma_{\alpha,s}[b_{2k}(\alpha, s)u_{\alpha s}f_\alpha(x) + d^\dagger{}_{2k}(\alpha, s)v_{\alpha s}f_\alpha{}^*(x)]$$

---

[11] The possible products may be enumerated by treating the set as a set of k-forms.
[12] These possible products may also be enumerated by treating the set as a set of k-forms.

The resulting total number of degrees of freedom (still respecting eqs. 3.6 and 3.7) is

$$d_{dr} = 2^{r/2 + 2} 2^{r/2 + 2} = 2^{r + 4} \qquad (3.14)$$

3.4.1 Internal Symmetries Factor Justification

The introduction of the internal symmetries factor increases the number of degrees of freedom for a space. The number of creation and annihilation operators specifies degrees of freedom primarily associated with fermion spin. Similarly the internal symmetries factor specifies the number of degrees of freedom associated with the set of internal symmetry groups. One must chose the range of internal symmetries index in eq. 3.10. The only apparent *a priori* choice for the range of internal symmetry k index in eq. 3.10 is

$$2^{r/2 + 2} \qquad (3.15)$$

This choice puts the degrees of freedom for the spin part of creation and annihilation operators on the same level as the degrees of freedom for internal symmetries. It gives an encouraging tightness of formulation. The choice is vindicated by the match between the r = 4 dimension array and the particle spectrums and set of internal symmetries of our Unified SuperStandard Theory.[13]

3.4.2 Dimension Array Features

The dimension r determines the number of components in a dimension array. *The dimensions within a dimension array are degrees of freedom.* Dimension arrays define the spaces of Cosmos Theory as shown in Fig. 3.1. As pointed out in previous books this number r plays two roles: 1) the overall dimension of the space and 2) within a dimension array it specifies the number of space-time dimensions of the space.

Having determined the dimension array for each even dimension r we may then proceed to allocate the fundamental fermion spectrum and the set of internal symmetries as well as other particle spectrums. In our four dimension universe our Unified SuperStandard Theory (UST) does this in detail. We have also specified the fermion spectrum and internal symmetries for higher dimension spaces as well.

The quadrupling pattern appearing in dimension arrays as the dimension r increases by two makes the determination of the form of higher dimension space-times easier. See chapter 4.

The form of dimension arrays, which is ultimately based on the number of independent antisymmetric tensors, is determined in the same manner as the form of γ-matrices.

3.5 The Nature of Dimension Arrays

The above derivation of γ-matrix form and dimension array form places them both as central to an understanding of elementary particles and space-times in our

---

[13] This match was the cause of our efforts in the study of hypercomplex spaces in the past five years beginning in Fall, 2019.

universe and other universes of higher dimension. It creates a basis for a truly unified theory of Nature, which our earlier books in the past four years demonstrate. It also provided a procedure in our recent books for the generation of the particles and symmetries of a space by General Relativistic-Internal Symmetry transformations from a single dimension in a Fundamental Reference Frame. Total Unification is achieved in 42 dimension and 88 dimension spaces.

COSMOS SPACES SPECTRUM

Blaha Space Number $N = o_s$	Cayley-Dickson Number n	Cayley Number d_c	Dimension Array column length d_{cn}	Dimension Array Size d_{dn}	Space-time-Dimension r
0	10	1024	2048	2048^2	18
1	9	512	1024	1024^2	16
2	8	256	512	512^2	14
3	7	128	256	256^2	12
4	6	64	128	128^2	10
5	5	32	64	64^2	8
6	4	16	32	32^2	6
7	**3**	**8**	**16**	$\mathbf{16^2}$	**4**
8	2	4	8	8^2	2
9	1	2	4	4^2	0
Limos :					
10	0	1	2	2^2	-2
11	-1	½	1	1	-4
12	-2	¼	½	$½^2$	-6
13	-3	1/8	¼	$¼^2$	-8
14	-4	1/16	1/8	$1/8^2$	-10

•
•
•
•

HYPERCOSMOS OF THE SECOND KIND SPACES SPECTRUM

Blaha Space Number $N = O_s$	Cayley-Dickson Number n	Cayley Number d_c	Dimension Array size d_{dN2}	Space-time-Dimension r	CASe Group $su(2^{r/2}, 2^{r/2})$ CASe
0	10	1024	1024×2048	18	su(512,512)
1	9	512	512×1024	16	su(256,256)
2	8	256	256×512	14	su(128,128)
3	7	128	128×256	12	su(64,64)
4	6	64	64×128	10	su(32,32)
5	5	32	32×64	8	su(16,16)
6	4	16	16×32	6	su(8,8)
7	**3**	**8**	$\mathbf{8 \times 16}$	**4**	**su(4,4)**
8	2	4	4×8	2	su(2,2)
9	**1**	**2**	2×4	**0**	su(1,1)
10	0	1	1×2	-2	
11	-2	½	½	-4	

Figure 3.1. The HyperCosmos, Limos, and the HyperCosmos of the Second Kind, space spectrums. Note $r = 2n - 2$.

4. Internal Quadrupling Structures

The n-forms, independent asymmetric tensors, γ-matrices, dimension arrays and Cosmos fractal curve all display a common internal quadrupling feature. We describe these features in this chapter. In general, when the dimension r, or the order n, increases by two for even r, or for order n, then the structure is quadrupled.

4.1 n-forms Quadrupling

When the even dimension r increases by two, the size 2^{n+2} of the resulting (n+2)-form is four times the size of the n-form 2^n. This is shown by example in section 2.8.1 with the detail described by eqs. 2.3 and 2.3a in particular.

$$T_n = T_{n-2} + 2\,T_{n-2}(1) + T_{n-2}(2) \qquad (2.3)$$

4.2 Asymmetric Tensor Quadrupling

For independent asymmetric tensors there is also a factor of four increase when the even dimension r increases by two, the size 2^{r+2} of the resulting set of dimension r+2 tensors is four times the size of the set of dimension r tensors 2^r by eq. 2.6.

4.3 γ-matrices Quadrupling

The γ-matrices that appear in the form of $\gamma^\mu \partial_\mu$ in fermion Dirac equations also display a quadrupling for even dimensions r when the dimension is increased by two. The number of γ^μ is r in dimension r. The matrices have $2^{r/2}$ by $2^{r/2}$ rows and columns. Fig. 4.1 illustrates the quadrupling effect for r = 4 (our universe) and for r = 6 (the Megaverse).

Case r = 2

There are three Pauli matrices. These matrices appear in the r = 4 case.

Case r = 4

The matrices exhibit a nested structure quadrupling as the dimension increases by 2. The r = 4 γ-matrices contain r = 2 Pauli matrices. The three Pauli matrices in the upper right and lower left quadrants for γ^i where i = 1, 2, 3. The Dirac γ^0–matrix, where $\gamma^4 \equiv \gamma^0 = \text{diag}(1, 1, -1, -1)$, connects the upper and lower parts of these γ-matrices. It is the analogue of the Connection group interactions of Cosmos Theory.[14] Connection groups connect the parts of the Cosmos particle spectrums just as γ^0 connects the parts of Dirac matrices. The quadrupling effect is evident. The connection γ^0 matrix ties the parts of Dirac matrices together. The connection γ^0 is not displayed in Fig. 4.1.

_____

[14] For Connection Groups see Appendix 9-B of Blaha (2023d). Connection Groups also appear in earlier books by the author.

Case r = 6

In fig. 4.1 the r = 6 diagram shows the form of four r = 6 Dirac matrices γ^μ where μ = 0, 1, 2, 3. In the four r = 6 γ-matrices, there are r = 4 γ^k matrices where k = 0, 1, 2, 3. Each γ^k (where k = μ) appears twice in each γ^μ matrix in opposing quadrants. For example, the r = 6 matrix for γ^3 is

$$\gamma^3 = \begin{array}{|c|c|} \hline \mathbf{0} & \begin{array}{c} \mathbf{DIRAC} \\ \gamma^3 \end{array} \\ \hline \begin{array}{c} \mathbf{DIRAC} \\ -\gamma^3 \end{array} & \mathbf{0} \\ \hline \end{array}$$

The number of these $2^{r/2}$ by $2^{r/2}$ γ-matrices in dimension r = 6 is r. We define two additional diagonal γ-matrices which we tentatively suggest may have a form analogous to the r = 4 case. Thus for r = 6 we take the additional two γ-matrices to be:[15]

$$\gamma^4 = \text{diag}(1, 1, -1, -1, -1, -1, 1, 1) \tag{4.1}$$
$$\gamma^5 = \text{diag}(1, 1, 1, 1, -1, -1, -1, -1)$$

They are not are not shown in Fig. 4.1. They correspond to the Connection groups of Cosmos Theory dimension arrays. They connect the γ-matrix parts in the four quadrants.

Case r > 6

For even dimensions r > 6 we define $\gamma_r{}^k$ as the kth γ-matrix in dimension r:

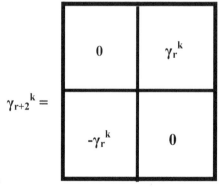

$$\gamma_{r+2}{}^k = \begin{array}{|c|c|} \hline \mathbf{0} & \gamma_r{}^k \\ \hline -\gamma_r{}^k & \mathbf{0} \\ \hline \end{array}$$

for k = 1, 2, ..., r − 1.

---

[15] Representations of these γ-matrices are equivalent up to a unitary transformation by Good's Theorem generalized to higher dimensions. See R. H. Good Jr., Rev. of Mod. Phys., **27**, 187 (1955).

In r + 2 dimensions, there are r γ-matrices $\gamma_{r+2}{}^\mu$ where $\mu = 0, 1, 2, \dots, r - 1$. Within these γ-matrices, there are $\gamma_r{}^k$ matrices where $k = 0, 1, 2, \dots, r - 1$. Each such $\gamma_r{}^k$ appears twice in each $\gamma_{r+2}{}^k$ matrix in opposing quadrants. These matrices total in number to r.

We define two additional diagonal γ-matrices which we tentatively suggest may have a form similar to the r = 4 case:

$$\gamma_{r+2}{}^r = \mathrm{diag}(\gamma_r{}^r, -\gamma_r{}^r) \qquad\qquad (4.2)$$
$$\gamma_{r+2}{}^{r+1} = \mathrm{diag}(1, 1, 1, 1, \dots, -1, -1, -1, -1, \dots)$$

where the number of 1's and -1's each have $2^{r/2}$ entries in $\gamma_{r+2}{}^{r+1}$. The number of entries total to $2^{(r+2)/2}$. The full set consists of (r + 2) $\gamma_{r+2}{}^\mu$ matrices where $\mu = 0, 1, 2, \dots, r + 1$.

Thus there is γ-matrix quadrupling with a pair of additional diagonal connection matrices added each time as r increases by 2.

4.4 Dimension Array Quadrupling

Dimension arrays quadruple in size as the dimension r increases by 2 due to eq. 3.11. Figs. 4.2 and 4.3 show the quadrupling effect, which nicely corresponds to the structure of the fermion spectrum.

The nesting quadrupling property carries through for the fermion spectrum and group symmetry arrays. Figs. 5.3 and 5.4 show the nested fermion structure.

The nesting of the group symmetries is modified after a quadrupling to connect various quarters together. Some of the symmetry groups are defined to connect quarters together using Connection Groups that we have described in earlier books such as Blaha (2023d). Connection groups parallel the connection γ-matrices described above that appear as the dimension r increases by two.

If one considers the known Standard Model part within these diagrams one sees it fits in the nested dimension arrays like the pieces in a puzzle. Thus there is experimental support for Cosmos Theory structuring in The Standard Model.

See Blaha (2023d) *Newton's Apple is Now the Fermion* and (2023e) *Cosmos Theory: The Sub-Particle Gambol Model* as well as our earlier books for additional detail.

4.5 Hilbert and Cosmos Fractal Curves Quadrupling

The quadrupling seen in γ-matrices and dimension arrays is paralleled in the form of Hilbert fractal curve and Fractal Cosmos[16] curve. These curves are very similar. The primary difference is Cosmos Dimension Array Column Length is twice the Hilbert Curve Line Length order by order of curve construction where the Dimension Array Cayley-Dickson number $n = n_H - 1$ with n_H being the Hilbert curve construction order.

---

[16] We use the name Cosmos Curve in preference to Cosmic Curve.

4.5.1 The Fractal Cosmos Curve

We now use the fractal relations first found in Blaha (2024b). The fractal construction of the Cosmos Curve is based on the association of dimension array column lengths[17] and the orders of piecewise linear line segment lengths that are used to form a fractal curve. Eq. 4.3 relates the *Cosmos Curve* construction to the Hilbert curve construction.[18]

Cosmos Cayley-Dickson number $n = n_H - 1$ (4.3)
Hilbert Curve Line Length $= 2^{n_H}$
Hilbert Number of "boxes" $= 2^{2n_H}$
Cosmos Dimension Array Column Length $= 2^{n+1} = 2^{n_H}$
Cosmos Dimension Array Size (number of elements in array) $= 2^{2n+2} = 2^{2n_H}$

where n is the Cosmos Cayley-Dickson number and n_H is the order in the Hilbert curve construction. A correspondence may be set up between Cosmos Dimension array diagrams and Hilbert curve line segment diagrams. Figs. 4.4 and 4.5 show the map between Cosmos Curve diagrams and equivalent Hilbert curve diagrams.

Non-negative n (or r) dimension array column lengths combine to generate a two dimension filled square fractal grid from a one dimension line segment.

The negative n (r) dimension array column lengths for n = -2 through n = -∞ combine to form a one dimension line element of length 1 equal to the array column length 1 for n = -1 from a zero dimension point due to the identity

$$\sum_{n=1}^{\infty} 2^{-n} = 1$$ (4.4)

If we adjoin the dimension array column lengths for n = −∞ through n = ∞ then we have the *Cosmos Curve from a zero dimension point to a two dimension filled square grid.*

The fractal dimension generation is paralleled by the generation of dimension arrays for spaces at each step in its construction.

4.5.2 The Two Dimension Square Grid Cosmos Curve

The Cosmos Curve generates a two dimension filled square grid. This grid might be viewed as the beginning of a new Cosmos spaces spectrum. It embodies the 4 dimensions of the 2×2 n = 0 dimension array d_{d0}, which is the precursor of the ten HyperCosmos spaces. It may be viewed as a continuous grid corresponding to d_{d0}.

The four corners of the Cosmos Curve square grid are mapped to the four dimensions of an n = 0 dimension array. We can associate that dimension array with the $n_H = 1$ Hilbert order diagram and proceed to construct a new Hilbert-like curve and new associated sets of Cosmos dimension arrays from it. At each order of construction we

---

[17] Order by order (dimension by dimension) the dimension array column lengths map to the length of the corresponding Hilbert curve piecewise line lengths. Blaha (2024b).
[18] The construction of the fractal curve corresponding to Cosmos Theory spaces was shown to be similar to the construction of the Hilbert feactal curve in Blaha (2024b).

take the boxes of type C in Fig. 4.4 and transform them to boxes of type D filling each with a "color pattern." As the order n_H increases, an irregularly shaped figure is generated that becomes a set of interconnected islands of "Cosmos" color.

This new construction of interconnected islands might be called a *SuperCosmos* archipelago. It corresponds order by order to supersets of Cosmos spaces with filled grids used to introduce continuity between dimensions in each 4 by 4 block. Thus a continuum is established between the elements of each diagram. The elements are, of course, Cosmos Theory sets of spaces.

4.5.3 Comparison between Fractal Formulation and Creation/Annihilation Operator Formulation

The fractal formulation, and the creation/annihilation operator based formulation, offer somewhat different approaches to Cosmos Theory. The fractal formulation, which has a Hilbert-like curve view of the Cosmos Curve, offers perhaps a simpler, more elegant formulation. The fractal formulation has the same nesting as the Cosmos Theory dimension arrays.

The fractal formulation does not have some significant features of the Creation And Annihilation Operator (CAA) formulation :

1.   ***The basis of the CAA formulation in the number of independent tensors singles out the CAA formulation as fundamental.***

2.   The choice of even number space-time dimensions only is natural in the CAA formulation since the total number of creation and annihilation operators in an odd dimension space equals the number in the next lower even dimension – thus giving a potential redundancy that is removed by choosing even dimensions only.

3.   The CAA formulation creates a dimension array that has extended General Relativistic – Internal Symmetry transformations that parallel the corresponding transformations of the creation/annihilation operators of fermion fields.in General Relativity.

4.   The CAA formulation allows one to define a Fundamental Reference Frame (FRF) that can map a single primordial dimension to complete dimension arrays, which introduces a fundamental simplicity into the Cosmos.

5.   Space-time dimensions may be extracted from a dimension array.

6.   Manipulation of the quantum fields based on the CAA formalism enables the creation of totally unified quantum field theories through the generation of 42 and 88 space-time dimension spaces. See Figs. 3.6 and 4.7.

We conclude the CAA tensor-based formalism is another basis for Cosmos Theory and the UST for our universe.

4.5.4 The Cosmos Curve and Unification and Fundamental Reference Frame (FRF)

In Blaha (2023a) we developed a unification of the ten HyperCosmos spaces and the 10 Second Kind HyperCosmos in a 42 space-time dimension Full HyperUnification space. See Fig. 3.1. The purpose was to create a space from these 20 spaces that supported a combined General Relativistic and symmetry group transformation that would generate the dimension arrays of all 20 spaces from one dimension located in a Fundamental Reference Frame (FRF).

In section 3.3.1 of Blaha (2023a) we described the nature of an FRF. A dimension array Reference Frame treats a dimension array with d_{dr} components as a vector. The vector is subject to a combined General Relativistic – Internal Symmetry transformation to produce a new dimension array in vector form. One may chose the Reference Frame to be an FRF where the vector has only one non-zero dimension. This FRF is analogous to the rest frame of a particle with only one non-zero momentum component: its energy equals its mass. The analogy to Special Relativistic transformations from a rest frame to a moving frame is clear.

Using FRF's allows the dimension array of any space to be reduced to one non-zero component.

An examination of Fig. 4.6 shows that the 10 dimension arrays' column lengths and 10 Second Kind HyperCosmos dimension arrays' column lengths combine to form the 42 space-time dimension Full HyperUnification space shown in Fig. 4.7. The column lengths of the HyperCosmos part are a subset of the column lengths in the Cosmos Curve. See Blaha (2023a) for details.

The dimension array of the 42 space-time dimension Full HyperUnification space can be treated as a vector in an 88 space-time dimension UltraUnification (UU) space. Then an FRF may be defined for it with only one non-zero dimension that enables the UU dimension array to be generated from the FRF with only one non-zero dimension.

Thus the UU enables a reduction of all Cosmos Theory dimension arrays to one primordial non-zero dimension – an ultimate form of unification of all Cosmos Theory spaces. See Fig. 4.7 for the structure of the complete set of Cosmos spaces. There are four levels in the Cosmos, which is the most economical approach to generating the Cosmos. The one primordial dimension in UU can be fractionated into an infinite dust of fractionated dimensions using Limos.

The spaces of Cosmos Theory (Fig. 4.7) *are*

> !0 HyperCosmos spaces + their 10 HyperUnification spaces +   (4.5)
> + !0 Second Kind HyperCosmos spaces +
> + the 10 Second Kind HyperUnification spaces +
> + the 42 Dimension Full HyperUnification Space +
> + the 88 Dimension UU space = 42 spaces

+ Limos[19](not shown in Fig. 4.7)

4.5.5 The Language of the Cosmos Curve

The Hilbert curve and thus the Cosmos Curve may be viewed as generated according to a language ((L System). The language specification is

Alphabet: α, β
Constants: φ + −
 Axiom: α

Production Rules:
α ⟶ +βφ–αφα – φβ+
β⟶ –αφ+βφβ+φα-

The language interpretation of the Hilbert and Cosmos Curves introduces an interesting new view of Cosmos Theory raising the issue of a Cosmos Language. Languages have been associated with Physics previously. See Blaha (1998) and (2005c) for detailed examples.

4.6 Analogous γ-Matrix – Dimension Array Features

The even space-time dimension γ-matrices exhibit properties similar to the Cosmos Theory dimension arrays:

1. Dimension arrays have a size that is 16 times the size of the corresponding γ-matrices.

2. The γ-matrices are square. They are r matrices of size $2^{r/2}$ by $2^{r/2}$. As the even space-time dimension r increases by 2 the γ-matrices row and column sizes double. The γ-matrices quadruple as a result. For example the r = 6 γ-matrices are 8 by 8 matrices containing a quadruple of r = 4 γ-matrix parts.

3. The γ-matrices exhibit a form of nesting in quadruples. Fig. 4.2 displays nesting from r =2 (Pauli matrices) to r = 4 and then to r = 6 quadrupling at each dimension increase by 2.

4. Fractional γ-matrices of *negative* dimension n may be defined by quartering the γ-matrices of the next higher space-time dimension. These fractional matrices may be of interest for gambol quantum field theory. This topic has been considered in our previous books.

---

[19] Limos spaces with their negative space-time dimensions are not part of the Full HyperUnification space or the UltraUnification space because they do not participate in the unification of the twenty HyperCosmos spaces.

The Hilbert curve features, Cosmos dimension array features, and γ-matrix structural features are the same.

4.7 Future Directions

The fundamental fact of Cosmos Theory, the number of independent tensors in a space, and the assumptions that then lead directly to the Cosmos spaces spectrum, make Cosmos Theory the most likely theory of the Cosmos.

This conclusion motivates the following program for Elementary Particles:

1. Study other additional features of Cosmos Theory.

2. Perform experiments to expand the fermion spectrum to a fourth generation and to three additional layers. Find the Dark Matter part.

3. Explore the implications of the Generation and Layer groups – particularly for the expansion of the Cabibbo-Kobayashi-Maskawa (CKM) matrix

4. Look for Astrophysical support for Cosmos Theory – particularly for the Megaverse and higher dimension universes.

The spectrum of particles and symmetries needs to be expanded from The Standard Model to the predictions of Cosmos Theory and the Unified SuperStandard Theory (UST).

Success in these endeavors will lead to a new Physics. The possibility of several new accelerators operating at 3 to 8 times current maximum energies is encouraging.

This author *solely* developed Cosmos Theory over the past five years beginning with The Unified SuperStandard Theory (UST) found in his previous work.

4.8 The Path of Investigation

The Standard Model →

      Unified SuperStandard Theory →

           Hypercomplex number based extensions →

                Cosmos Theory →

                      Fractal Cosmos Curve Theory →

                            Tensor based Fractal Cosmos Theory

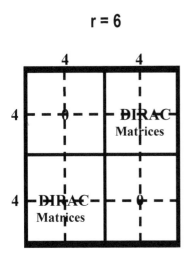

Figure 4.1. The γ-matrices for r = 4 and r = 6 space-time dimensions. The matrices exhibit a nested structure quadrupling as the dimension increases by 2. For example, the r = 4 γ-matrices contain the r = 2 Pauli matrices. The r = 4 diagram shows the three Pauli matrices in the upper right and lower left quadrants. The $\gamma^0 = \gamma^4 = diag(1, 1, -1, -1)$ matrix is not shown. The r = 6 diagram shows four Dirac matrices with each in a quadrant. There are two additional γ-matrices. See sections 4.3. and 4.4. The additional γ-matrices that are not shown correspond to the Connection groups of Cosmos Theory dimension arrays. They connect the parts in γ-matrix quadrants.

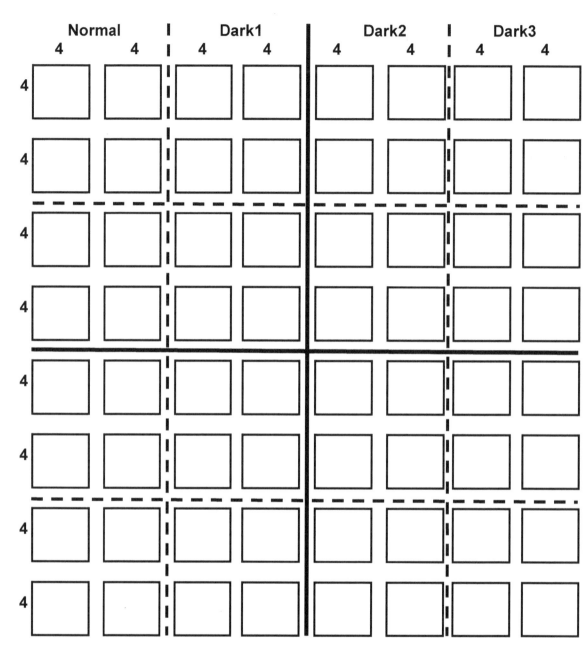

Figure 4.2. The n = 4 (where r = 6) Megaverse dimension array. Four quadruplings are visible. Each quadrant is an n = 3 (r = 4) UST dimension array. There is a visible substructure. There are sixty-four 4 × 4 n = 1 blocks. Each 8 × 8 quadrant is an n = 2 dimension array. Each 16 × 16 quadrant is an n = 3 dimension array. An exact match with Hilbert orders nesting is evident. This figure is from Blaha (2020d) for the Megaverse. Note r = 2n – 2. See Fig. 3.1.

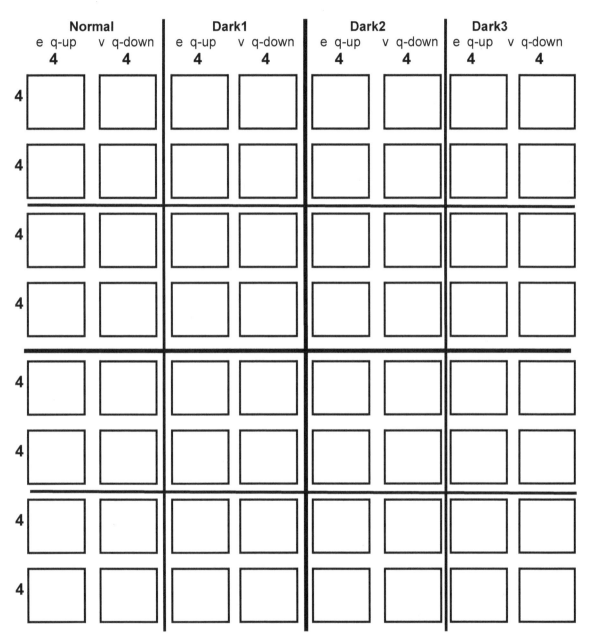

Figure 4.3. Partition of the fermion 32 × 32 Cayley-Dickson n = 4 (Megaverse) dimension array. Four quadruples are visible. There are sixty-four 4 × 4 n = 1 blocks. Each 8 × 8 quadrant is an n = 2 dimension array. Each 16 × 16 quadrant is an n = 3 dimension array. An exact match with Hilbert orders is evident. The label e q-up indicates a charged lepton – up-type quark pair. The label v q-down indicates a neutral lepton – down-type quark pair, and so on. This figure is from Blaha (2020i) for the UST and Megaverse. Note r = 2n – 2. See Fig. 3.1.

$n_H = 1$ Hilbert Line

A

Extend to make a Cosmos Cayley-Dickson n = 0 Dimension Array Box (of 4 dimensions)

B

Hilbert Order $n_H = 2$ Fractal View, a Cayley-Dickson n = 1 Dimension Array Box (of 16 dimensions)

C

Hilbert Order $n_H = 2$ and n = 1 Cosmos View

D

Cosmos Cayley-Dickson n = 1 Dimension Array Form (of 16 dimensions)

E

Figure 4.4. The transition from the Hilbert curve Fractal diagrams to the Cosmos Theory dimension array diagrams. Every Hilbert fractal diagram has an equivalent Cosmos Theory dimension array.

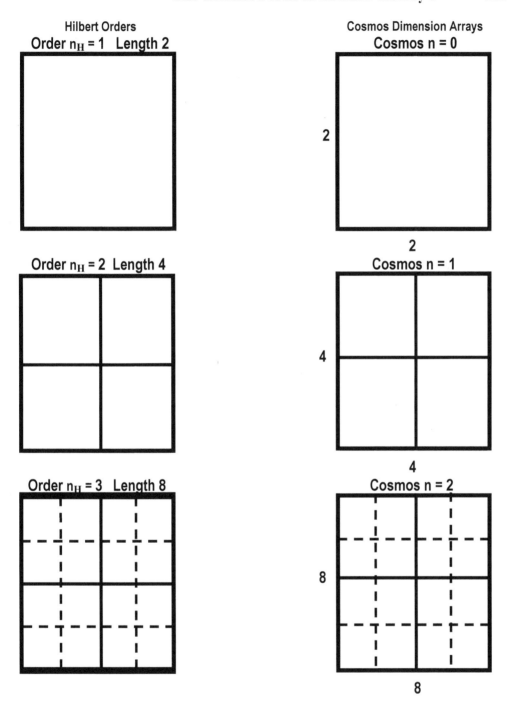

Figure 4.5. Low order Hilbert line segments depicted as nested sets of boxes as in Fig. 4.4 compared to corresponding Cosmos Theory dimension arrays ordered by Cayley-Dickson numbers. Dimension array sizes are displayed.

Figure 4.6. Form of a HyperUnification transformation. It is also the form of the dimension array of 42 dimension space-time. Ten HyperCosmos dimension array's column lengths are shown. Ten Second Kind HyperCosmos dimension array's column lengths are contained in the d_{cB} by d_{cB} block. The figure is not drawn to scale. See Chapter 6 of Blaha (2023a) for details.

Figure 4.7. Diagram of the four levels of the Cosmos Spaces. They contain 42 spaces with no contributions from Limos spaces which are treated separately.

5. Dimension Array Decomposition

The dimension array for dimension r has

$$2^{r+4} \tag{5.1}$$

components. Within it are

$$2^{r+1} \tag{5.2}$$

parts consisting of 8 real-valued dimensions for one of the direct products

$$
\begin{aligned}
&SU(4)\\
&SU(2)\otimes U(1)\otimes SL(2, \mathbf{C})\\
&U(4)\\
&SU(2)\otimes U(1)\otimes SU(2)\otimes U(1)
\end{aligned} \tag{5.3}
$$

according to Figs. 5.1 and 5.2 below.

We now decompose dimension arrays into an array totaling 2^{r+1} elements. Each element consists of 8 real-valued dimensions.

$$d_{nr} = 8 \sum_{i=1}^{2^{r+1}} d_i = 2^{r+4} \tag{5.4}$$

where

$$d_i = \text{the } i^{th} \text{ element in the dimension array} \tag{5.5}$$

The γ-matrices appear in Dirac equations in the form $\gamma \cdot \partial$. Similarly we create an ordered set of internal symmetry irreducible representation matrices, T_{imj} ordered in the same way as the elements in d (for matrix indices m and j).

The d_i are sets of 8 real-valued dimensions for irreducible representations of internal symmetries. We may identify the d_i as representing parts of fermion wave functions (See section 5.1 for more details.) with internal symmetry indices k appearing in CAA operators in eq. 3.13 such as $b_{1k}(\alpha, s)$. Each d_i represents a set of values of k.

We can form internal symmetry representations.[20] The form of this combination of dimension array parts and internal symmetry matrices T_i may be represented by

$$T_{imj}d_i \tag{5.6}$$

---

[20] Note that the parts consist of direct products. Consequently the corresponding matrices must be treated similarly.

where the T_{imj} and d_i are formed from the respective representation internal symmetry matrices T_i irreducible representation, and the corresponding dimensions in d_i with i labeling the internal symmetry. We then form the products with vector boson wave functions $A_m{}^\mu$

$$A_i{}^\mu T_{imj} \tag{5.7}$$

to represent terms in corresponding fermion Dirac equations with d_i representing coordinates within fermion wave functions.[21]

Thus each set of dimension array parts, d_i, maps to the wave function indices of internal symmetries. A dimension array represents a set of internal symmetry dimensions that maps directly to internal symmetry matrices.

Similarly, the γ-matrices of a space separate into parts such as the individual γ^μ matrices. The similarity of γ-matrices, and dimension arrays combined with internal symmetry irreducible representation matrices, is evident.

---

[21] We note again that the d_i represent subsets of a fermion's wave function's internal symmetry indices (eq. 3.13).

5.1 Details of the Transition from the d_i to Interaction Terms

The definition of internal symmetry interaction terms based on the d_i parts of a dimension array is based on the general form of fermion wave functions (eq. 3.13):

$$k = 1 \qquad\qquad b_{p1}(\alpha, s) \qquad\qquad d^\dagger_{p1}(\alpha, s)$$
$$2 \qquad\qquad b_{p2}(\alpha, s) \qquad\qquad d^\dagger_{p2}(\alpha, s)$$

$$\cdots \qquad\qquad\qquad\qquad \cdots$$

[a set of d_{ij} dimension wave function terms for internal symmetry i]

$$\cdots \qquad\qquad\qquad\qquad \cdots$$

$$\psi_{pk}(x) \;\; = \ldots b_{pk}(\alpha, s) \ldots \qquad + \qquad d^\dagger_{pk}(\alpha, s) \; \ldots \qquad\qquad (5.8)$$

$$\cdots \qquad\qquad\qquad\qquad \cdots$$

$$2^{r+4} \qquad\qquad b_{p2^{r+4}}(\alpha, s) \qquad\qquad d^\dagger_{p2^{r+4}}(\alpha, s)$$

where the internal symmetry index is k, where the last wave function above has internal symmetry index 2^{r+4}, and where p = 1, 2 is the PseudoQuantum index.

When an internal symmetry matrix T_i is combined with a wave function, then the internal symmetry indices of the matrix T_{imj} combine with the corresponding internal symmetry indices of the wave function:

$$\sum_j T_{imj}\psi_{2j} \;\; = \;\; \sum_j T_{imj}\psi_{2j} \qquad\qquad (5.9)$$
$$\text{j contained}$$
$$\text{in } d_i$$

where 2 is the PseudoQuantum index (chosen arbitrarily) and i labels the internal symmetry with matrix indices m and j. Then the interaction term in field equations is

$$A_i{}^\mu T_{imj}\psi_{2j} \equiv A_i{}^\mu T_i\psi_2$$

5.2 Tentative Experimental Confirmation

An examination of Fig. 5.3 shows that the d_1 part of the dimension array is exactly The Standard Model. One expects the next part that will be found is d_2. They would appear in the analysis of the four generation version of the Cabibbo-Kobayashi-Maskawa (CKM) matrix.

Significant confirmation would involve discovery of fourth generation fermions, three additional layers of fermions, and the discovery of Dark matter fermions.

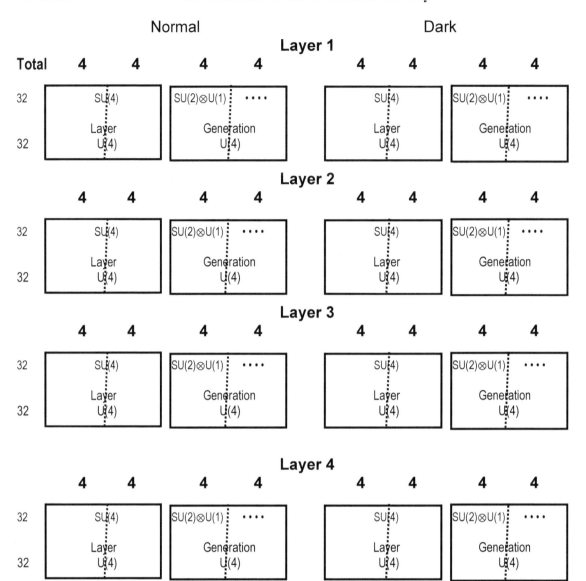

Figure 5.1. Schematic for the Normal and Dark symmetries of UST. The real and imaginary dimensions are counted separately. For example SU(4) has four real dimensions and four imaginary dimensions. Each layer has 32 + 32 = 64 dimensions. There are 256 dimensions corresponding to the 256 entries in the dimension array for UST where n = 3. The 32 • 's form sets of 4 dimensions were initially allocated to 4D space-times. These dots are mapped to SL(2, **C**) and 7 SU(2)⊗U(1) Connection groups. Three groups unite layers, and 4 groups unite corresponding Normal and Dark layers This figure is from Blaha (2020d) for the UST.

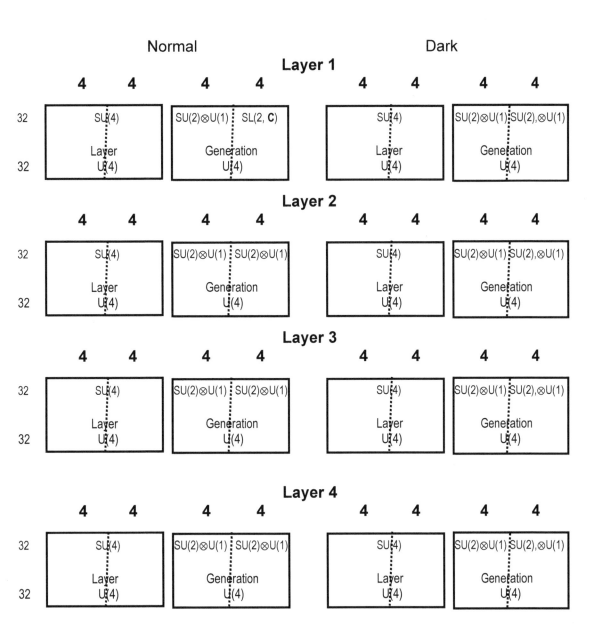

Figure 5.2. Schematic for the Normal and Dark symmetries of UST. Seven sets of dots in Fig. 5.1 are replaced by SU(2)⊗U(1) Connection groups. SL(2, C) represents the Lorentz group SO⁺(1,3). This figure is from Blaha (2020d) for the UST.

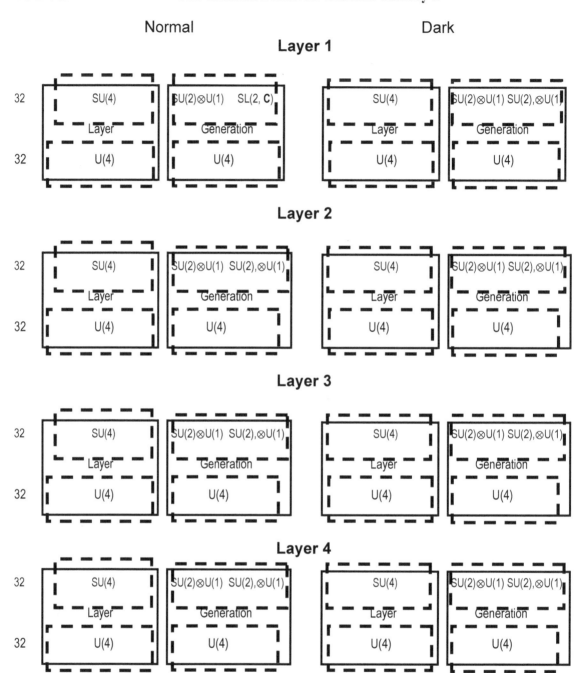

Figure 5.3. The thirty-two 8 dimension d_i parts of the r = 4 UST dimension array. The r = 6 dimension array (not shown) has 128 8 dimension d_i parts.

6. Cosmos Spaces and UST

The Cosmos Theory spectrum of spaces (Fig. 3.1) does not create universes. The spectrum is a template for the structure of universes. A space is a structure without substance. Universes must be defined/created separately. The creation of a universe requires an initial mass/energy. Universes are composed of substances. They begin as a state (A Big Bang state it seems) that unfolds according to a structure specified by the dimension array for its space-time dimension. A dimension specifies the universe's structure. Within the dimension array for a universe there are dimensions for internal symmetry groups and space-time dimensions. The space-time dimensions within a dimension array total to the dimension of the space.[22]

The sequence of events leading eventually to universes is

Define a sequence of integers n

For each n, one can define a set of independent asymmetric tensors

Generate a spectrum of spaces

Then derive the size of the dimension arrays for each space.

Use the dimension array to define internal symmetries' fundamental representations dimensions and space-time dimensions

Use the quadrupling feature to extrapolate from the internal symmetries to the structure of higher dimension spaces

Generate one or more universes

6.1 Generation of the Cosmos Universes[23]

The definition of the Cosmos spaces does not, in itself, specify any universes. A universe is a structure containing mass-energy. It must be generated. It uses a Cosmos space structure as a template. We have developed quantum field theories of universes with interactions in previous books. These theories are renormalizable in any dimension to any order in perturbation theory using the author's Two Tier formalism of Blaha (2002).

There are a number of ways to generate universes:

---

[22] Thus the 10 dimensions used to define the set of 10 Cosmos spaces also appear within the dimension arrays.
[23] Parts of this section and subsequent sections appeared in Blaha (2024b).

1. Generate all universes *ab initio.*

2. Generate the top Parent universe of 18 space-time dimensions. Within that universe sub-universes may be generated through universe interactions.

3. Generate universes from vacuum states.

Once a set of universes is generated, universes may interact dynamically with universes being created or destroyed in quantum processes. It is then possible for the set of universes to achieve an equilibrium. Blaha (2024a) considered such a set of universes and found a model with a 23 universe distribution. See Figs. 6.1 and 6.2.

      The physical laws within universes determine their evolution. See our previous books for details.

6.2 Cosmos Theory Brought to the Simplest Formulation
      The formulation of Cosmos Theory has been reduced to the simplest terms:

1. A primordial point is the primitive term;

2. A direct generalization to a scale independent set of piecewise linear curves that combine to produce a fractal, Hilbert-like infinite curve – the postulate;

3. At each order of construction a set of dimensions (dimension array) is defined that specify a space. A space's extent is variable within a parent universe;

4. Universes may be defined as quantum field states;

5. Universes of different spaces may interact.

The procedure for creating the Cosmos parallels the creation process of Euclid's Geometry. It may be viewed as strictly mathematical – leading to the dynamics of interacting universes and particles within universes. The Unified SuperStandard Theory (UST) is one of the results.[24]

        Cosmos Theory is a complete Cosmology based on pure number.

6.3 Unified SuperStandard Theory
      This author developed Cosmos Theory in the past 5+ years based on the prior development of the Unified SuperStandard Theory (UST) in the preceding 20 years.[25]

---

[24] The UST was developed over the past 23 years by this author. It led to hypernumber quantum theories and then to Cosmos Theory.

[25] The UST is based on Two Tier quantization (2003) to eliminate perturbation theory infinities, on PseudoQuantization, which the author developed in the 1970's, and on higher derivative quantum field theories for quark confinement and modified divergence-free gravitation.

Five years ago the author noticed a correspondence between the UST with its 256 fermion spectrum (Figs. 6.3 and 6.4), and the UST's 256 fundamental representation internal symmetry and space-time dimensions (Figs. 5.1 and 5.2), with a Cayley number 256. These features led to the author's development of Cosmos Theory.

Over the past five years the features of Cosmos Theory were developed in detail including its unification mechanism, its pattern of Cosmos Space features, and its fundamental basis.

The close, detailed, agreement between the $r = 4$ Cosmos Theory space structure and the UST is circumstantial evidence for Cosmos Theory. Exploration of higher dimension spaces is not possible as yet although there is suggestive data of possible external universes' influences on the structure of our universe. The Standard Model with its successes fits very beautifully within the $r = 4$ dimension array structure. When new fermions and their symmetries are found, then there is reason for hope that the UST will be fully vindicated, and Cosmos Theory supported.

If our universe does not have Dark Matter, a possibility, then our universe would implement a HyperCosmos space of the Second Kind.

6.4 UST Source of the Distributions of Energy, Normal Matter and Dark Matter in the Various Numbers of Particle Species

The UST has a wide range of predictions: new generations of fermions, new layers of fermions, new internal symmetries, and a Dark Matter sector. The realization of these possibilities seems somewhat unlikely at present or near term available accelerator energies.

Thus it is reasonable to examine the global possibilities due to the 256 elements in the Unified SuperStandard Theory (UST) (Cayley-Dickson number 3 Cosmos space in Fig. 3.1). These possibilities center on the relative proportions of normal and Dark matter and the distribution of energy.

We base this analysis on an equipartition of mass and energy between their various species and modes.[26]

6.5 Equipartition Principle for Particle Degrees of Freedom

In a closed system at equilibrium the thermal energy of a system is equally partitioned (distributed) among its degrees of freedom. This Equipartition Principle is well known. The application of this principle to the beginning of the universe *when all particles were massless* and all symmetries were unbroken suggests that the distribution of mass-energy should be the same for all degrees of freedom at that time. Thus there should be approximately equal numbers and energies of fermions and vector bosons with the same fraction of the total thermal energy.

We now estimate the relative proportion of Normal and Dark matter in the universe at its beginning based on this Equipartition Principle.

---

[26] Equipartition of mass and energy in Blaha (2016a) and (2018e).

6.6 Proportion of Dark Mass-Normal Mass in the Universe

First we note that 24 of the 64 fermion species (counting quarks of each color as a separate species) in layer 1 of UST – the layer with which we are familiar are Normal matter fermions. (Our discussion is based on our Unified SuperStandard Theory.) Forty of the 64 first layer species are Dark.

The other three fermion layers are all Dark from our point of view since they have not been detected. Thus we find that 232 of the 256 fermion species are Dark yielding a *percentage of Dark Matter equal to 232/256 = 91.1%*.

Recent studies of the proportion of Dark Matter in the universe have yielded an estimate: 85% of the total mass.

Thus our rough estimate based on our fermion Equipartition Principle is approximately the same as the experimental estimate. The disparity may be due to the decay of Dark fermions to Normal fermions over time.

6.7 Proportion of Dark Mass-Energy in the Universe

We know of 12 of the 256 vector boson dimensions in the Unified SuperStandard Theory dimension array are associated with known interactions and 24 out of 256 fermions are Normal. Thus we find a total of 476 out of 512 degrees of freedom are Dark yielding a Dark mass-energy of 93% of the universes mass-energy at the beginning of the universe.

The sum of Dark energy in the universe currently has been estimated to be 68.2% of the total energy and the energy of Dark Matter is estimated to be 26.8%. The total is 95% - a value that compares favorably with our above approximate estimate of 93%. The difference in these values can be attributed to various factors. One distinct possibility is the decay of Dark mass-energy from higher layers to the known layer in the 13.8 billion years since the Big Bang.

6.8 Implications of Approximate UST Match with Experiment

The approximate match suggests the dimension array of 256 dimensions is correct as opposed to the much smaller Standard Model results. It also supports the UST proportions of Normal and Dark fermions, and the proportions of known and Dark internal symmetries—global support for the UST matching the detailed support for the UST fermion and internal symmetry spectrums. It also buttresses the validity of Cosmos Theory.

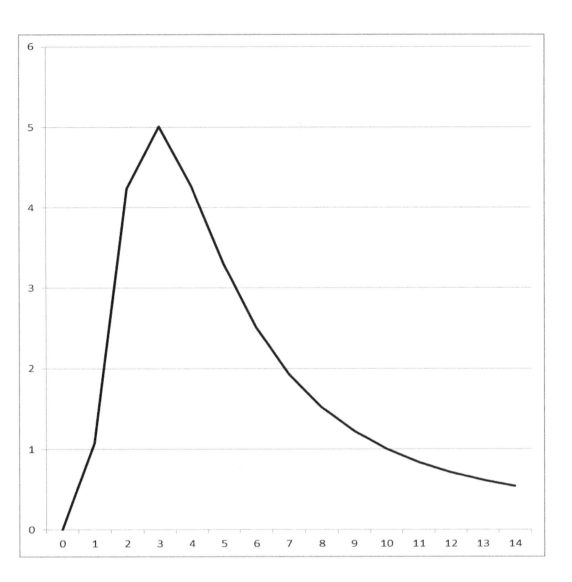

Figure 6.1. Plot of $U_g(\varepsilon(n))$ vs. the Cayley-Dickson number n. $[U_g(\varepsilon(10))] = 1$ by design. The number of universes for n > 10 is zero: $[U_g(\varepsilon(n))] = 0$ for n > 10. Small n corresponds to larger s and T_g. Large n corresponds to smaller s and T_g. The jagged curve is the result of "coarse graining" n. Fig. 11.2 shows the numbers of universes $[U_g(\varepsilon(10))]$ is 23 with one Blaha Number N = 0 parent universe and 22 "gambol" universes. See Blaha (2024a).

UNIVERSE NUMBERS

n	1	2	3	4	5	6	7	8	9	10	11
$[E_g]$	1	4	5	4	3	2	1	1	1	1	0

Figure 6.2. Table of Cayley-Dickson number n vs. the number of universes, $[U_g(\varepsilon(n))]$. Note there are no universes for HyperCosmos spaces n > 10. Thus Cosmos Theory may be limited to ten HyperCosmos spaces with this model. The universe of type n = 1 have zero space-time dimensions and 16 components in their dimension arrays. There is no n = 0 universe. See Fig. 10.1 of Blaha (2024a).

Normal   **Dark**

4   4   4   4

Layer 1

Generation

1	e q-up	v q-down	e q-up	v q-down
2	μ q-up	v q-down	μ q-up	v q-down
3	τ q-up	v q-down	τ q-up	v q-down
4	e' q-up	v q-down	e' q-up	v q-down

Layer 2

Generation

1	e q-up	v q-down	e q-up	v q-down
2	μ q-up	v q-down	μ q-up	v q-down
3	τ q-up	v q-down	τ q-up	v q-down
4	e' q-up	v q-down	e' q-up	v q-down

Layer 3

Generation

1	e q-up	v q-down	e q-up	v q-down
2	μ q-up	v q-down	μ q-up	v q-down
3	τ q-up	v q-down	τ q-up	v q-down
4	e' q-up	v q-down	e' q-up	v q-down

Layer 4

Generation

1	e q-up	v q-down	e q-up	v q-down
2	μ q-up	v q-down	μ q-up	v q-down
3	τ q-up	v q-down	τ q-up	v q-down
4	e' q-up	v q-down	e' q-up	v q-down

Figure 6.3. Periodic table for the Normal and Dark fermions of UST. Each fermion corresponds to a dimension. Subscripts of neutrinos and quarks are not shown. A fourth generation is indicated for each layer. There are 256 fermions corresponding to the 256 entries in the dimension array for n = 3. This figure is from Blaha (2020d) for the UST. The nesting in 4×4 blocks is evident within 8×8 blocks within a 16×16 block.

Figure 6.4. Fermion particle spectrum and partial example of pattern of mass mixing of the Generation and Layer grroups. Unshaded parts are the known fermions including an additional, as yet not found, 4th generation shown. The lines on the left side (only shown for one layer) display the Generation mixing within each layer's species. The Generation mixing applies within each layer using a separate Generation group for each layer. The lines on the right side show Layer group mixing with the mixing amongst all four layers for each of the four generations individually. There are four Layer groups. For each generation and each layer, SU(2)⊗U(1) mixes between an e-type fermion and a neutrino-type fermion. It also mixes between an up-quark-type fermion and a down-quark-type fermion. SU(3) mixes among each up-quark triplet and down-quark triplet separately. Complex Lorentz group transformations map among all four fermions: Dirac ↔ tachyon ↔ up-quark ↔ down-quark There are 256 fundamental fermions counting quarks as triplets. This figure is from Blaha (2020e) for the UST.

7. Fractal Cosmos Curve Decomposition

The Cosmos Curve is constructed from a mathematical point to a unit line segment and then to a two-dimension unit square grid. The construction from a mathematical point to a line segment relies on the sum:

$$\sum_{n=1}^{\infty} 2^{-n} = 1 \qquad (4.4)$$

The terms in this summation correspond directly to ½ of the length of columns d_c in the Cosmos Theory spectrum for negative space-time dimensions. We have called this part of the Cosmos spectrum Limos. See Fig. 3.1.

We then construct the remainder of the fractal Cosmos Curve from line segments that order by order are of length equal ½d_c for the HyperCosmos spaces in Fig. 3.1.

Thus the fully adjoined sequence of dimension array column lengths for $n = -\infty$ through $n = \infty$ gives a *Cosmos Curve from a zero dimension point to a two dimension filled square grid.*

The Cosmos Curve is a mathematical construct. We assume the column lengths corresponding to Cayley-Dickson numbers n define the rows and columns d_{cn} of Cosmos space dimension arrays. Cosmos space dimension arrays are not substances. They are abstract definitions of sets of dimensions. As such they conceptually correspond to the lengths of Cosmos Curve line segments.

7.1 Map from Cosmos Curve Two Dimension Grid to Cosmos Theory Spaces

We now construct a relationship between a position (x, y) within the unit square of dimension two with the corresponding Cosmos space dimension array size d_{dr}. We propose the relation:

$$d_{dr} = 2^{r+4} = 2^{8/(x+y)} \qquad (7.1)$$

where the coordinates x and y are confined to a two dimension unit grid by:

$$0 \le x + y \le 2 \qquad (7.2)$$
$$0 \le x \le 1$$
$$0 \le y \le 1$$

Eq. 7.1 implies the relation between x and y and the space-time dimension r:

$$x + y = 8/(r + 4) \qquad (7.3)$$

or

$$r = 8/(x + y) - 4 \qquad (7.4)$$

We note:

$$\text{If } x + y = 2 \qquad r = 0$$

$$\text{If } x + y = 1 \qquad r = 4$$

$$\text{If } x + y = 0 \qquad r = \infty$$

7.1.1 The Main Sequence of Cosmos Spaces

If we set $x = y$ to view the diagonal, which we call *The Main Sequence of Cosmos Spaces*, we find

$$\text{If } x = 1 \qquad r = 0$$

$$\text{If } x = \tfrac{1}{2} \qquad r = 4$$

$$\text{If } x = 0 \qquad r = \infty$$

giving a diagonal line for x and y for the entire HyperCosmos spectrum (where $r \geq 0$) with

$$r = 4/x - 4 \qquad (7.5)$$

See Fig. 7.1. The 10 spaces of the HyperCosmos have even r values ranging from $r = 0$ to $r = 18$. The value of x corresponding to $r = 18$ is $x = 2/11$. Therefore the set of HyperCosmos spaces correspond to the x range [2/11, 1].

7.1.2 The Other Diagonal

If we set $x + y = 1$ then we find

$$\text{If } x = 1 \text{ and } y = 0 \qquad r = 4$$

$$\text{If } x = y = \tfrac{1}{2} \qquad r = 4$$

$$\text{If } x = 0 \text{ and } y = 1 \qquad r = 4$$

giving the square grid's other diagonal line for x and y that has $r = 4$ for all x and y where $x + y = 1$. See Fig. 7.2. *This diagonal gives a certain prominence to r = 4, the dimension of our universe.*

7.2 Continuity of the x = y Main Sequence Diagonal in the Unit Cosmos Grid

The Main Sequence diagonal in the Cosmos Curve grid interpolates between the space-time dimensions r of HyperCosmos spaces. By eq. 7.5 we find

$$x = 4/(r + 4) \qquad (7.6)$$

The HyperCosmos values of r, which is even, select a set X of corresponding x values ranging from 0 (r = ∞) through 1 (r = 0). Thus we can use this square grid diagonal to obtain a continuous line of r values for spaces intermediate between HyperCosmos spaces[27] and extending to r = ∞. Between the spaces in the Main Sequence of Cosmos spaces are spaces that provide transitions between Cosmos Theory spaces. These spaces might play a role if travel between universes were ever to become feasible. Chapter 12 considers "travel" between spaces via intermediate dimensions.

7.3 The Cosmos Grid

The points of the two dimension square grid, that we call the *Cosmos Grid*, generated by the fractal Cosmos Curve specify possible Cosmos spaces. We start with the y = x diagonal which we call the *Main Sequence of Cosmos spaces*. The Cosmos spaces points within the Cosmos Grid for the Limos spaces are described in section 8.3.

7.3.1 Cosmos Grid points for HyperCosmos Spaces

The Cosmos Grid points for HyperCosmos spaces are given by eqs. 7.6 and 7.5. See Fig. 7.3 for a depiction.

7.3.2 Cosmos Grid points for HyperCosmos Spaces of the Second Kind

The Cosmos Grid points for HyperCosmos spaces of the Second Kind have the values

$$x = 4/(r + 3) \tag{7.7}$$

Their dimension is

$$r = 4/x - 3 \tag{7.8}$$

The size of their associated dimension arrays is

$$d_{dr} = 2^{r+3} = 2^{4/x} \tag{7.9}$$

7.3.3 Cosmos Grid Points for Cosmos Unification Spaces

The Cosmos Grid points on the Main Sequence of Cosmos spaces of the 88 Dimension UltraUnification Space and the 42 Dimension Full HyperUnification Space (Fig. 4.6) are

$$x = 1/23 \tag{7.10}$$

and

$$x = 2/23 \tag{7.11}$$

respectively.

7.3.4 Cosmos Grid Points for Cosmos Spaces

The Cosmos Grid points corresponding to Cosmos spaces are:

---

[27] Renormalization theory studies by 't Hooft, Veltman and others have used fractiona dimensions near 4.

HyperCosmos Spaces   where $x = 4/(r + 4)$

$\underline{r}$	$\underline{x}$
0	1
2	2/3
4	½
6	2/5
8	1/3
...	
18	2/11
...	
∞	0

Second Kind HyperCosmos Spaces $x = 4/(r + 3)$

$\underline{r}$	$\underline{x}$	
0	4/3	Off the unit grid
2	4/5	
4	4/7	
6	4/9	
8	4/11	
...		
18	4/21	
...		
∞	0	

Unification Spaces $x = 4/(r + 4)$

42	2/23	42 Dimension Full HyperUnification Space
88	1/23	88 Dimension UltraUnification Space

Limos spaces x points are described in section 8.3.

7.4 Correspondence Between Cosmos Curve and Internal Symmetries

The Cosmos Curve naturally leads to HyperCosmos dimension arrays, which, in turn, leads to the dynamical Internal Symmetry interactions as shown in chapter 5. We can symbolize this relation with

Cosmos Curve → Square Grid → d_{dr} → dimension array → internal symmetry interactions

Correspondingly, we found the transitions in chapter 5:

dimension array parts → internal symmetry parts → internal symmetries → interaction terms

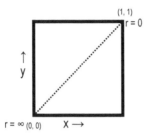

Figure 7.1. Square Cosmos Grid with a diagonal connecting r = 0 and r = ∞.

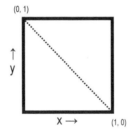

Figure 7.2. Square grid with a diagonal with each point corresponding to r = 4. These diagonals intersect at x = y = ½ where r = 4.

8. Growing Dimensions Incrementally

This chapter considers growing the dimensions of a space in a continuous manner incrementally. It begins with a discussion of the Cosmic Curve's square unit grid's derivatives. Then it considers growing a dimension from r to r + 1 in increments within the framework of the grid and also within HyperCosmos spaces.

8.1 Derivatives of Dimensions

The continuity of the grid diagonal in the x and y variables (eqs. 7.1 – 7.5) leads us to consider derivatives of d_{dn} and space-time dimension r:[28]

$$\partial d_{dn}/\partial x \quad \text{and} \quad \partial d_{dn}/\partial y \tag{8.1}$$

and

$$\partial r/\partial x \quad \text{and} \quad \partial r/\partial y$$

From eqs. 7.1 and 7.4 we find

$$\partial r/\partial x = \partial r/\partial y = -8/(x+y)^2 \tag{8.2}$$

$$\partial d_{dn}/\partial x \, \partial d_{dn}/\partial x = \partial r/\partial y \, \partial d_{dn}/\partial r \tag{8.3}$$

$$= -8/(x+y)^2 \, 2^{8/(x+y)}$$

and similarly for derivatives with respect to y. Note eqs. 8.2-8.3 imply that r increases as x + y decreases. Eq. 8.3 implies that the Cosmos' dimension array d_{dn} has an essential singularity at x + y = 0. All derivatives of d_{dn} with respect to x and/or y are infinite at x + y = 0.

8.2 Creation/Growth of Dimensions

As one traverses the x = y curve in the Cosmos Curve grid we find the dimension r continuously increases from zero to ∞ as x + y decreases to zero. It raises the question: How do the dimensions increase?

8.2.1 Simply Adding an Additional Dimension

One possibility is to consider the coordinate "3" dimension as growing out of a two dimensional surface. One cannot directly infinitesimally grow the third dimension from the two dimension surface. For an infinitesimal insertion makes the surface three dimensional regardless of being "infinitesimal."

---

[28] The constant n is related to r by r = 2n − 2.

8.2.2 Adding Additional Dimensions by Group Direct Products

So, in the above example, we must consider a growth path through infinitesimals that keeps the surface two-dimensional plus infinitesimal increments of a third dimension.

The spaces of the Limos sector of Cosmos Theory spaces appear to offer a solution. We note

$$d_{cn} = 2^{r/2+2} \qquad (8.4)$$

where r is the dimension. Thus $r = 2\ln_2(d_{cn}) - 4$. We now define a new Limos space $s_i(r_{in})$ of dimension r_{in} where[29]

$$r_{in} = d_{cn}/4 = 2^{r/2} \qquad (8.5)$$

for $r < 0$. This dimension is the r_{in} column in Fig. 8.1. The space $s_i(r_{in})$ may be taken to correspond to an orthogonal group $O(r_{in})$ of dimension r_{in} where the orthogonal group definition is extended to fractional dimensions.[30]

Then we may take a space of dimension r and increment it with s_i incrementally starting with $s_i(1/2)$ and proceeding to add to $s_i(\infty)$. The summation of the r_{in} values is one by eq. 4.4 above. The product ("summation") of the infinitesimal groups totals one unit.

For example, a sum (based on eq. 4.4) of incremental growths in dimension then may be represented as

$$SO(1, r) \otimes O(2^{-1}) \otimes O(2^{-2}) \otimes \ \ldots \otimes O(2^{-\infty}) \to SO(1, r + 1) \qquad (8.6)$$

where $O(r)$ represents the orthogonal group in a space of dimension r. The set of groups in eq. 8.6 is a subgroup of $SO(1, r + 1)$ as indicated.

Thus we obtain a space with $r + 1$ spatial dimensions. While the space is incrementing the space effectively has a fractional dimension.

The increment process adds a sequence of infinitesimal dimensions. This process may be taken to a continuous limit. Thus the $x = y$ grid diagonal may be realized as continuous in dimensions—based on an extension of the Limos definition of spaces for negative values of r.

---

[29] Section 3.4.2 points out "The dimension r determines the number of components in a dimension array. *The dimensions within a dimension array are degrees of freedom.* Dimension arrays define the spaces of Cosmos Theory as shown in Fig. 3.1. As pointed out in previous books this number r plays two roles: 1) the overall dimension of the space and 2) within a dimension array it specifies the number of space-time dimensions of the space." Thus the choice of dimension for a space is a matter of definition. For $r \geq 0$ we chose $r_{dimension\ array} = r$. We chose $r_{dimension\ array} = r_{in}$ for negative dimensions r.

[30] We have considered groups with fractional dimensions in past books for the case of the unitary groups.

8.3 Cosmos Grid Extension to Limos Spaces

The spaces of the Limos sector of Cosmos Theory may be mapped to the Cosmos Grid using the dimension r_{in} in eq. 8.5. With this definition of dimension we find

$$r_{in} = 8/(x + y) - 4 \tag{8.7}$$

If we assume the *Main Sequence of Cosmos spaces*: $y = x$ then

$$r_{in} = 4/x - 4 = 2^{r/2} \tag{8.8}$$

where r is the space-time dimension column in Fig. 8.1 and

$$x = 4/(r_{in} + 4) = 4/(2^{r/2} + 4) \tag{8.9}$$

Some x, r_{in} and r values for Limos spaces

$$\begin{array}{ccc} r & x & r_{in} \\ \hline -2 & 8/9 & \frac{1}{2} \\ -4 & 16/17 & 1/4 \\ & \cdots & \\ -\infty & 1 & 0 \end{array} \tag{8.10}$$

Thus the Limos spaces have x values ranging from 8/9 to 1 on the Cosmos Grid Main Sequence.

Blaha Space Number	Cayley-Dickson Number	Cayley Number	Dimension Array column length	Dimension Array Size	Space-time-Dimension	Incremental Dimension
$N = o_s$	n	d_c	d_{cn}	d_{dn}	r	r_{in}
Limos :						
10	0	1	2	2^2	-2	$\frac{1}{2}$
11	-1	$\frac{1}{2}$	1	1	-4	$\frac{1}{4}$
12	-2	$\frac{1}{4}$	$\frac{1}{2}$	$\frac{1}{2}^2$	-6	1/8
13	-3	1/8	$\frac{1}{4}$	$\frac{1}{4}^2$	-8	1/16
14	-4	1/16	1/8	$1/8^2$	-10	1/32

Figure 8.1 Limos Sector of the Cosmos Theory set of spaces from Fig. 3.1. Note the additional r_{in} column.

8.4 Growth of the Cosmos Curve

We now consider growing the Cosmos Curve order by order incrementally. The orders of piecewise linear line segment lengths in the construction of a Cosmos Curve are related to the Hilbert curve construction in chapter 4:[31]

Cosmos Cayley-Dickson number $n = n_H - 1$ (4.3)
Hilbert Curve Line Length $= 2^{n_H}$
Hilbert Number of "boxes" $= 2^{2n_H}$
Cosmos Dimension Array Column Length $= 2^{n+1} = 2^{n_H}$
Cosmos Dimension Array Size (number of elements in array) $= 2^{2n+2} = 2^{2n_H}$

where n is the Cosmos Cayley-Dickson number and n_H is the order in the Hilbert curve construction.

We can create an infinitesimal growth sequence from order to order using eq. 4.4 above by infinitesimal increments:

$$2^{n+1} \rightarrow 2^{n+2}$$

where the increments are

$$2^{n+1-k}$$

for $k = \infty$ through 1 based on the identity

$$2^{n+1} \sum_{k=1}^{\infty} 2^{-k} = 2^{n+1} \qquad (8.11)$$

The incremental growth in piecewise linear line segment lengths follows from order to order of the Cosmos Curve.

---

[31] The construction of the fractal curve corresponding to Cosmos Theory spaces was shown to be similar to the construction of the Hilbert fractal curve in Blaha (2024b).

9. Generation of Cosmos Theory Spaces from the Cosmos Grid

The HyperCosmos spaces of Cosmos Theory can be generated from the fractal Cosmos Curve. Thereby, we obtain a full specification of dimensions of the HyperCosmos Spaces starting from a zero dimension point.

Our goal was to start with the simplest possible origin—a zero dimension point that a Creator might choose and then proceed to create the Cosmos. The search for simplicity dates back to Pre-Socratic times in the West.

9.1 Dimensions of Stages in the Construction of the Cosmos Curve

We start with a zero dimension point and then use eq. 4.4 to generate a one dimension unit line segment. Then we follow a fractal construction process to create a two dimension unit square grid.

The unit square grid encompasses all the HyperCosmos spaces within it.

9.2 Extraction of Dimension Arrays of HyperCosmos Spaces

We then use the fractal grid decomposition process described in chapter 7 to extract the dimension array size d_{nr} for all HyperCosmos spaces. Thus we have the almost complete set of Cosmos spaces.

9.3 HyperCosmos Spaces of the Second Kind

The remaining spaces of Cosmos Theory, Limos spaces and HyperCosmos spaces of the Second Kind, may be generated in the unification process summarized in Fig. 4.7. See section 7.3.2 for the Cosmos Grid points of HyperCosmos spaces of the Second Kind.

9.4 Limos Sector Spaces

See section 8.3.

9.5 Cosmos Unification Spaces

See section 7.3.3 for the Cosmos Grid points of Cosmos Unification spaces.

9.4 Universes

The Cosmos Theory structure built in the above outlined manner may then be used in the construction of universes either by a creator or dynamically as discussed earlier in this book.

Thus we have generated a Cosmos from a Mathematical point.

10. Origin of the Tenth Cosmos Space and Universe

Our choice of the r = 18 space as the original Parent universe raises several issues. There can be no time before the definition of the Parent space dimension array since no space or universe existed before its definition. Yet a Parent universe cannot exist without the definition of the Parent's dimension array. Thus the dimension array and Parent universe must be simultaneously defined and created.

The only way that one may reasonably resolve this state of affairs is to define both as the consequence of a consistency condition. We suggest the consistency condition for the minimum Parent universe dimension is the requirement that its virtual thermodynamic outward pressure equals the Casimir vacuum inward pressure from its virtual external vacuum Casimir pressure at the point of origin of the virtual universe.[32] See Fig. 10.1. Below this minimum dimension the Parent universe cannot exist since the virtual vacuum pressure will cause it to be contracted into non-existence.

The dimension r of the Parent universe fixes a maximum Physical Cosmos space dimension.[33] Within the Parent universe there are universes of lower dimension corresponding to lower dimension Cosmos spaces.

10.1 Balance Between Expansion and Contraction

When a potential virtual universe is "virtually" created it may expand (Hubble expansion) or it may contract to a point and then cease to exist. The decision is based on the dynamics of the virtual creation. Does the virtual universe possess sufficient mass-energy to generate a pressure for expansion or does the potential surrounding[34] virtual vacuum pressure causes the universe to contract and be "snuffed out"?

The balance between inward and outward pressure can be represented as

$$H = P - C \qquad (10.1)$$

where P is the pressure of the energy-momentum contents of the virtual universe and C is the Casimir force due to the virtual vacuum energy embodied in the surface of the universe. There are three possibilities:

$H < 0$	Casimir force causes contraction to a point	(10.2)
$H = 0$	Balance of forces - stability	
$H > 0$	Pressure causes (Hubble) expansion of universe	

---

[32] Much of this chapter is based on Blaha (2022d) and (2023e).
[33] Depending on whether the Parent universe is non-expanding (r = 18) or expanding (r = 20). We discuss this issue later.
[34] In the *surface* of the virtual universe.

We wish to use H to determine the Cosmos Theory spectrum. At first view, it has a lower limit at r = 0 but no apparent upper limit. We now view H as determining the maximum dimension r_{Parent} of the Physical Cosmos spectrum:

$$H \geq 0 \quad \text{"Normal" universe } r \leq r_{Parent} \qquad (10.3)$$
$$H < 0 \quad \text{Virtual universe lapses into non-existence}$$

We now proceed to determine H for the space of dimension r.

Figure 10.1. Schematic diagram of universe's empty vacuum bubble showing the confining Casimir force of the exterior vacuum. This force is countered by internal fermion gas pressure symbolized by a jagged interior star.

10.2 Number of Fundamental Particle Species

Cosmos Theory specifies the number of fundamental fermion species N for a universe in a space of dimension r:

$$N = 2^{r+4} \qquad (10.4)$$

The determination of the maximum number of fermions from H will fix the maximum dimension r.

10.3 Conditions at the Consistency Point

We now consider an infinitesimal box containing the energy-momentum of a virtual universe. The box contains fermions with the initial features:

1. All fermions are massless.
2. Their interactions are zero.
3. All baryon numbers are zero.

10.4 Thermodynamic Outward Pressure

We tentatively base the thermodynamic pressure on the Ideal Gas Law

$$P = NkT/V \qquad (10.5)$$

where P is the pressure, T is the temperature, k is Boltzmann's constant, and N is the number of particles in volume V.

Assuming the fermion gas occupies a spherical spatial ball with spatial volume

$$V_{r-1} = \pi^{(r-1)/2}a^{(r-1)}/\Gamma((r-1)/2 + 1) \qquad (10.6)$$

with radius a in an r dimension space-time:

$$P = N\,\Gamma((r-1)/2 + 1)kT/(\pi^{(r-1)/2}a^{(r-1)}) \qquad (10.7)$$

where $\Gamma(n)$ is the factorial function. The number of fermions N is given by eq. 10.4.

10.5 Casimir Effect Confining Force

This section calculates the force on a universe due to the Casimir effect.[35] We assume the universe is in a vacuum energy bubble in an r – 1 dimension spatial region of radius a. It generates a confining force on the surface of the universe. We start with the infinite Dirac fermion vacuum energy per unit volume:

$$U_\infty = \int_0^\infty d^{r-1}k\ (k^2 + m^2)^{1/2} \qquad (10.8)$$

where m is the common fermion mass, which we take to be zero by section 10.3.

Due to the vacuum-less bubble, the vacuum energy changes to

$$U = U_\infty - U_{bubble} \qquad (10.9)$$

where the missing bubble vacuum energy per unit volume is

$$U_{bubble} = \int_d^\infty d^{r-1}k\ (k^2 + m^2)^{1/2} \qquad (10.10)$$

where d is the momentum space lower limit of the excluded vacuum energy within the bubble. The Casimir deficit is

$$U = \int_0^d d^{r-1}k\ k \qquad (10.11)$$

Assuming the momentum d corresponds to the spatial radius, a, of the bubble $d \sim a^{-1}$ we find the energy deficit per unit volume is

---

[35] H. G. B. Casimir, Koninkl. Ned. Adak. Wetenschap. Proc. **51**, 793 (1948), S. K. Lamoreaux, Phys. Rev. Lett. **78**, 5 (1997), L. S. Brown and G. J. McClay, Phys. Rev. **184**, 1272 (1969), and references therein.

$$U \cong \pi^{(r-1)/2} a^{-r} (r-1)/[r\Gamma((r-1)/2 + 1)] \tag{10.12}$$

Multiplying by the volume of the bubble we find a total bubble energy;

$$U_{tot} \approx V_{r-1} U \tag{10.13}$$

$$\approx \pi^{r-1} a^{-1}[(r-1)/r]/\Gamma((r-1)/2 + 1)^2 \tag{10.14}$$

Then

$$\partial U_{tot}/\partial a \cong -\pi^{r-1} a^{-2}[(r-1)/r]/\Gamma((r-1)/2 + 1)^2 \tag{10.15}$$

The bubble surface of radius a has the area

$$S_{r-2} = 2\pi^{(r-1)/2} a^{r-2}/\Gamma((r-1)/2) \tag{10.16}$$

The Casimir force on surface is

$$C = (S_{r-2})^{-1} \partial U_{tot}/\partial a \tag{10.17}$$

$$= -\tfrac{1}{2} \pi^{(r-1)/2} a^{-r} [(r-1)/r] \Gamma((r-1)/2)/\Gamma((r-1)/2 + 1)^2$$

$$= -\pi^{(r-1)/2} a^{-r}/[r\Gamma((r-1)/2 + 1)]$$

10.6 H Balance

We now set the outward pressure of the internal fermion "gas" equal to the inward Casimir vacuum force by eqs. 10.7 and 10.17:

$$H = P - C$$
$$= N \Gamma((r-1)/2 + 1)kT/(\pi^{(r-1)/2}a^{(r-1)}) - \pi^{(r-1)/2} a^{-r}/[r\Gamma((r-1)/2 + 1)] \tag{10.18}$$

Eliminating common factors in H we find the

$$H' = N akT - \pi^{(r-1)}/[r\Gamma((r-1)/2 + 1)^2] \tag{10.19}$$

At the critical point of eq. 10.2 we see H' = 0 implying

$$N = \pi^{(r-1)}/[arkT \Gamma((r-1)/2 + 1)^2] \tag{10.20}$$

For collapse H' < 0

$$N < \pi^{(r-1)}/[arkT \Gamma((r-1)/2 + 1)^2] \tag{10.21}$$

For expansion H' > 0

$$\dot{N} > \pi^{(r-1)}/[arkT \Gamma((r-1)/2 + 1)^2] \tag{10.22}$$

10.7 N and H' as Functions of Dimension r
We find that the choice of

$$akT = 2.635 \times 10^{-10} \qquad (10.23)$$

and the Cosmos dimension array size choice $N = 2^{r+4}$, give a critical point at dimension r = 18.   Thus a stable, non-expanding r = 18 Parent universe could exist.

Below r = 18 we find H' is negative indicating such a Parent universe could not exist. The Casimir force prevents its existence. At r = 18 the pressure and Casimir force are equal thus allowing an 18 dimension Parent universe within which child universes may be created. The r = 18 virtual universe is the minimal (in r) universe, and thus the Parent universe.

On this basis we can choose a Physical set of ten Cosmos spaces. We can create one or more 18 dimension Parent universes. Each Parent universe is stationary. It balances expansion and contraction. A parent universe can contain universes of lesser Cosmos dimension.

If we wish the Parent universe to be *expanding* then we can choose the r = 20 space's universe as the Parent universe. This choice would expand the Physical set of HyperCosmos spaces to eleven.

10.8 Support for the Power Series Form of Dimension Arrays
The size of dimension arrays N is a power series in 2 as shown in eq. 10.4. If we take eq. 10.20 and use Stirling's approximation for the gamma function a power series emerges with exponent r for large values of r.

Stirling's approximation is

$$n! = (2\pi n)^{\frac{1}{2}} \; (n/e)^n \qquad (10.24)$$

For large r >> 1, $n \cong r/2$ and

$$\Gamma((r-1)/2 + 1) \rightarrow (\pi r)^{\frac{1}{2}}(r/2e)^{r/2}$$

Substituting in eq. 10.20 gives

$$
\begin{aligned}
N &= \pi^{(r-1)}/(arkT) \times 1/(\pi r(r/2e)^r) \\
&= (2e\pi/r)^r/(\pi arkT) \\
&= (17.08/r)^r/(\pi arkT)
\end{aligned}
\qquad (10.25)
$$

It shows the same form of power series with exponent r as N in eq. 10.4. The similarity in form, which is based on the form of volume and surface area in higher dimension spaces, reflects their joint basis in differential forms, n-forms and wedge expressions, seen in chapter 2.

We see a strengthening of the view of dimension array sizes as based on geometry.

10.9 Why Ten Physical HyperCosmos Spaces?

An examination of eq. 10.25 shows that there is a critical point in the values of N due to the factor

$$(2e\pi/r)^r$$

where the number $2e\pi/r$ transitions from greater than one to less than one at $r = 2e\pi = 17.08$. At this value of r and thus at $r = 18$ the Casimir force changes from greater than the thermodynamic pressure to less than the thermodynamic pressure OR from contraction to expansion of the Parent universe. Thus $r = 18$ marks the beginning of an acceptable Parent universe since $r < 18$ would give a universe that contracts to a point and thus could not generate child universes.

The key scale for universe and thus space dimension is $2e\pi$. We view this result as a confirmation of the approach in this chapter and the choice of $r = 18$ as the largest possible Physical HyperCosmos space as well as of the 10 Physical HyperCosmos space spectrum.

10.10 Possible Temperature Dependence on r

If we assume a temperature dependence on the dimension r and set

$$N = 2^{r+4} = (2e\pi/r)^r/(\pi ark T) \qquad (10.26)$$

we find

$$kT = (e\pi/r)^r/(16\pi ar) = (8.54/r)^r/(16\pi ar) \qquad (10.27)$$

indicating a temperature power series that peaks at $r \cong 8$.

11. The Chain of Cosmos Development

Cosmos theory as it has evolved is the result of a significant series of stages. In this chapter we list the some of the stages with comments.

Cosmos Structure	Comment
Mathematical Point	
Fractal Cosmos Curve	
Separation of Curve Line Segments	
Map to the Dimensions of Spaces	
Separation of Cosmos Two Dimension Grid into Infinitesimal dimension growth	
Map of Dimensions to totally Asymmetric Tensors	
Map of Total Numbers of these Tensors to Dimension Array Sizes	
Spaces – Space-Time and Internal Symmetry dimensions	
Dimension Structure of spaces based on quadrupling	Assumption based on asymmetric tensor and n-form structure
Choice of certain spaces as structuring universes – 10 spaces	Arbitrary
Map of elements of each space to Internal Symmetry group dimensions	Based on Standard Model
Choice of some groups to be Connection Groups	To unite fermion sectors
Map of some elements to space-time dimensions	
Unification of Internal Symmetries and Space-time in two composite spaces	
Use of a Fundamental Reference Frame to reduce the number of dimensions to one	
Result: A comprehensive Structure without Substance	

Cosmos Universes	Comment
Substances as Energy-Matter Composites	
Universe Structure defined by a space structure	
Universes have mass-energy when created	
Universes begin as a point particle	
Universes begin by expansion (Big Bang)	
Universes are particles with a QFT with interactions	
One universe is the parent of all other universes	May be more than one parent
Universes have an internal dynamics based on space symmetries	Space structure determines dynamics

Particle Interactions	Comment
In our universe, Unified SuperStandard Theory (UST)	consistent with r = 4 space dimension array
Universes of higher dimension spaces – quadrupling versions of UST	assumption
Higher dimension particles – quadruplings of UST	assumption
Higher dimension life – possible but chemically different	assumption

The above list specifies the process that the author pursued in the 5+ years since 2019. In the course of this investigation the author examined many possible alternatives.

12. Travel between the Universes of Cosmos Spaces

The square grid of the Cosmos Curve has continuous coordinates x and y that smoothly connect spaces of differing dimensions. These spaces may have associated universes. It is conceivable that, in some distant future, travel between universes might be possible. The dimensions of these universes and spaces, space-time and internal symmetry, may be varied continuously. In chapter 7 we considered the infinitesimal growth of dimensions from space to space—universe to universe. For humanity to travel between universes of different dimension it would be necessary to encapsulate human explorers within four dimension cocoons.

The development of a mechanism for such transits between spaces and universes remain to be done. This author has previously considered the possibility of travel from our universe to an enclosing outer universe by using "cracks" in the surface tension of our universe due to large gravitational masses. We considered uniships for inter-universe travel.

Travel between our universe and an enclosing universe raises the issue of the location of the "edge of the universe." The edge of the universe is every point of the universe. This fact may be understood by considering a two dimension flat (or almost flat) surface within a three dimension universe. Every point on the two dimension surface is at the edge of the enclosing three dimension universe.

The edge of our universe is *everywhere* within our universe. Finding a mechanism for escape from our universe is the *only* challenge (other than accommodating human occupants.).

12.1 Energy Requirements for Uniships[36]

We have seen that the Theory of Relativity and Quantum theory have led to the fission of heavy nuclei to smaller nuclei to produce energy. They have also led to the fusion of small nuclei such as Hydrogen to form heavier nuclei that also produce energy.

Looking to the distant future and Humanity's quest to go to the stars [and beyond] it appears that there is a need for a more potent, more compact form of energy generation if we can look to an inter-star-based civilization. The most energetic possible energy source that we can consider today is starship propulsion based on electron-positron annihilation. We see streams of magnetically bottled electrons intersecting with streams of magnetically bottled positrons to propel starships.

However, electron-positron annihilation does not appear to be a sufficient fuel source for starships. If a new fuel source were available, then speedy travel to the stars [and beyond the universe] becomes possible. See Blaha (2011b) and (2014c).

---

[36] This section and the following sections are from Blaha (2022d).

12.2 Faster-than-Light Travel

The possibility of faster-than-light travel was considered in earlier books by the author. Gerald Feinberg, and others, raised the possibility seriously as a Physics question in 1968. He concluded there was no conflict between faster-than-light Physics and "normal" Physics. This author confirmed this point in detail in his books including a confirming study of Thermodynamics and Statistical Mechanics. See Blaha (2018e) and its Appendix H on Thermodynamics.

12.3 Alternative Fuel Source

The speed of light is a "stop sign" *not* a "show-stopper." The problems are the fuel and the engine. The most significant problem for faster-than-light starships (and conventional rocketry) is maximizing the energy content of fuel.

We could consider bottled quark – bottled anti-quark based propulsion. That could be a major improvement if quark bottling were achievable. Ultimately this also does not seem to be capable of supporting rapid transit to the stars.

12.4 Vacuum Propulsion using NilSpace Bubbles

Based on the fractionated gambol studies presented earlier, it appears that a bottled *NilSpace* bubble, within which the Fermi-Dirac sea of charged fermions has been removed [or much lessened], may offer the best propulsion system for rapid interstellar transit. We call this type of bubble a *NilSpace* since its charged fermion sea contents are absent (or nearly absent.) This possibility is at best an ultimate hope for a distant future. Nevertheless, the consideration of this possibility seems to be a worthwhile endeavor.

It appears that the most significant technology required for vacuum propulsion is super-ultrastrong magnetic fields sufficient to remove the charged fermion Fermi-Dirac Sea in a "bubble" region or at least a substantial part thereof creating a NilSpace.

We can imagine a *macroscopic* (but not necessarily large) region in space, from which the Dirac seas of charged fermions has been removed by super-ultrastrong magnetic fields.

An estimate of the NilSpace energy stored in a bubble (sphere) in our universe of radius a is

$$E = 4/3\ \pi a^3\ U \approx 4/3\ \pi^2 a^{-1} \tag{12.1}$$

This NilSpace region would have an ultra-large relative energy – much beyond a region of electron-positron annihilation. One might think of the region as a super-large positron-like particle in the sense that a positron is a "hole" in the vacuum. A super-positron would be a macroscopic "hole" in the vacuum that is stabilized and controlled by super-magnetic fields that could allow a type of graduated decay that generates an energy stream - thrust.

Having such a NilSpace ("hole") region, one could enable the region to shrink by siphoning streams of particles directed to furnish thrust to a starship. See Fig. 12.1.

The siphoning process would cause the bubble to uniformly shrink. The siphon creates a thrust that is a superposition of particles and a corresponding filled fermion sea neighborhood. The directed particles furnish thrust.

Thereby rapid transit to the stars [and other universes] may become possible. Needless to say this proposal is presently very far from realization. But it is a hope for the distant future! Or perhaps sooner?

Figure 12.1.   Schematic of a NilSpace bubble engine generating a siphoned stream to produce thrust. As vacuum is "siphoned in" through the orifice the bubble shrinks and a stream of positive energy fermions "flows" out providing propulsion. Controlling magnets and surrounding starship are not shown.

REFERENCES

Akhiezer, N. I., Frink, A. H. (tr), 1962, *The Calculus of Variations* (Blaisdell Publishing, New York, 1962).

Bjorken, J. D., Drell, S. D., 1964, *Relativistic Quantum Mechanics* (McGraw-Hill, New York, 1965).

Bjorken, J. D., Drell, S. D., 1965, *Relativistic Quantum Fields* (McGraw-Hill, New York, 1965).

Blaha, S., 1995, *C++ for Professional Programming* (International Thomson Publishing, Boston, 1995).

_____, 1998, *Cosmos and Consciousness* (Pingree-Hill Publishing, Auburn, NH, 1998 and 2002).

_____, 2002, *A Finite Unified Quantum Field Theory of the Elementary Particle Standard Model and Quantum Gravity Based on New Quantum Dimensions™ & a New Paradigm in the Calculus of Variations* (Pingree-Hill Publishing, Auburn, NH, 2002).

_____, 2004, *Quantum Big Bang Cosmology: Complex Space-time General Relativity, Quantum Coordinates™ Dodecahedral Universe, Inflation, and New Spin 0, ½, 1 & 2 Tachyons & Imagyons* (Pingree-Hill Publishing, Auburn, NH, 2004).

_____, 2005a, *Quantum Theory of the Third Kind: A New Type of Divergence-free Quantum Field Theory Supporting a Unified Standard Model of Elementary Particles and Quantum Gravity based on a New Method in the Calculus of Variations* (Pingree-Hill Publishing, Auburn, NH, 2005).

_____, 2005b, *The Metatheory of Physics Theories, and the Theory of Everything as a Quantum Computer Language* (Pingree-Hill Publishing, Auburn, NH, 2005).

_____, 2005c, *The Equivalence of Elementary Particle Theories and Computer Languages: Quantum Computers, Turing Machines, Standard Model, Superstring Theory, and a Proof that Gödel's Theorem Implies Nature Must Be Quantum* (Pingree-Hill Publishing, Auburn, NH, 2005).

_____, 2006a, *The Foundation of the Forces of Nature* (Pingree-Hill Publishing, Auburn, NH, 2006).

_____, 2006b, *A Derivation of ElectroWeak Theory based on an Extension of Special Relativity; Black Hole Tachyons; & Tachyons of Any Spin.* (Pingree-Hill Publishing, Auburn, NH, 2006).

_____, 2007a, *Physics Beyond the Light Barrier: The Source of Parity Violation, Tachyons, and A Derivation of Standard Model Features* (Pingree-Hill Publishing, Auburn, NH, 2007).

_____, 2007b, *The Origin of the Standard Model: The Genesis of Four Quark and Lepton Species, Parity Violation, the ElectroWeak Sector, Color SU(3), Three Visible Generations of Fermions, and One Generation of Dark Matter with Dark Energy* (Pingree-Hill Publishing, Auburn, NH, 2007).

_____, 2008a, *A Direct Derivation of the Form of the Standard Model From GL(16) (Pingree-Hill Publishing, Auburn, NH, 2008).*

_____, 2008b, *A Complete Derivation of the Form of the Standard Model With a New Method to Generate Particle Masses Second Edition* (Pingree-Hill Publishing, Auburn, NH, 2008)

_____, 2009, *The Algebra of Thought & Reality: The Mathematical Basis for Plato's Theory of Ideas, and Reality Extended to Include A Priori Observers and Space-Time Second Edition* (Pingree-Hill Publishing, Auburn, NH, 2009).

_____, 2010a, *Operator Metaphysics: A New Metaphysics Based on a New Operator Logic and a New Quantum Operator Logic that Lead to a Mathematical Basis for Plato's Theory of Ideas and Reality* (Pingree-Hill Publishing, Auburn, NH, 2010).

_____, 2010b, *The Standard Model's Form Derived from Operator Logic, Superluminal Transformations and GL(16)* (Pingree-Hill Publishing, Auburn, NH, 2010).

_____, 2010c, *SuperCivilizations: Civilizations as Superorganisms* (McMann-Fisher Publishing, Auburn, NH, 2010).

_____, 2011a, *21st Century Natural Philosophy Of Ultimate Physical Reality* (McMann-Fisher Publishing, Auburn, NH, 2011).

_____, 2011b, *All the Universe! Faster Than Light Tachyon Quark Starships & Particle Accelerators with the LHC as a Prototype Starship Drive Scientific Edition* (Pingree-Hill
Publishing, Auburn, NH, 2011).

_____, 2011c, *From Asynchronous Logic to The Standard Model to Superflight to the Stars* (Blaha Research, Auburn, NH, 2011).

_____, 2012a, *From Asynchronous Logic to The Standard Model to Superflight to the Stars volume 2: Superluminal CP and CPT, U(4) Complex General Relativity and The Standard Model, Complex Vierbein General Relativity, Kinetic Theory, Thermodynamics* (Blaha Research, Auburn, NH, 2012).

_____, 2012b, *Standard Model Symmetries, And Four And Sixteen Dimension Complex Relativity; The Origin Of Higgs Mass Terms* (Blaha Reasearch, Auburn, NH, 2012).

_____, 2013a, *Multi-Stage Space Guns, Micro-Pulse Nuclear Rockets, and Faster-Than-Light Quark-Gluon Ion Drive Starships* (Blaha Research, Auburn, NH, 2013).

_____, 2013b, *The Bridge to Dark Matter; A New Sibling Universe; Dark Energy; Inflatons; Quantum Big Bang; Superluminal Physics; An Extended Standard Model Based on Geometry* (Blaha Reasearch, Auburn, NH, 2013).

_____, 2014a, *Universes and Megaverses: From a New Standard Model to a Physical Megaverse; The Big Bang; Our Sibling Universe's Wormhole; Origin of the Cosmological Constant, Spatial Asymmetry of the Universe, and its Web of Galaxies; A Baryonic Field between Universes and Particles; Megaverse Extended Wheeler-DeWitt Equation* (Blaha Reasearch, Auburn, NH, 2014).

_____, 2014b, *All the Megaverse! Starships Exploring the Endless Universes of the Cosmos Using the Baryonic Force* (Blaha Research, Auburn, NH, 2014).

_____, 2014c, *All the Megaverse! II Between Megaverse Universes: Quantum Entanglement Explained by the Megaverse Coherent Baryonic Radiation Devices – PHASERs Neutron Star Megaverse Slingshot Dynamics Spiritual and UFO Events, and the Megaverse Microscopic Entry into the Megaverse* (Blaha Research, Auburn, NH, 2014).

_____, 2015a, *PHYSICS IS LOGIC PAINTED ON THE VOID: Origin of Bare Masses and The Standard Model in Logic, U(4) Origin of the Generations, Normal and Dark Baryonic Forces, Dark Matter, Dark Energy, The Big Bang, Complex General Relativity, A Megaverse of Universe Particles* (Blaha Research, Auburn, NH, 2015).

_____, 2015b, *PHYSICS IS LOGIC Part II: The Theory of Everything, The Megaverse Theory of Everything, U(4)⊗U(4) Grand Unified Theory (GUT), Inertial Mass = Gravitational Mass, Unified Extended Standard Model and a New Complex General Relativity with Higgs Particles, Generation Group Higgs Particles* (Blaha Research, Auburn, NH, 2015).

_____, 2015c, *The Origin of Higgs ("God") Particles and the Higgs Mechanism: Physics is Logic III, Beyond Higgs – A Revamped Theory With a Local Arrow of Time, The Theory of Everything Enhanced, Why Inertial Frames are Special, Universes of the Mind* (Blaha Research, Auburn, NH, 2015).

_____, 2015d, *The Origin of the Eight Coupling Constants of The Theory of Everything: U(8) Grand Unified Theory of Everything (GUTE), S^8 Coupling Constant Symmetry, Space-Time Dependent Coupling Constants, Big Bang Vacuum Coupling Constants, Physics is Logic IV* (Blaha Research, Auburn, NH, 2015).

_____, 2016a, *New Types of Dark Matter, Big Bang Equipartition, and A New U(4) Symmetry in the Theory of Everything: Equipartition Principle for Fermions, Matter is 83.33% Dark, Penetrating the Veil of the Big Bang, Explicit QFT Quark Confinement and Charmonium, Physics is Logic V* (Blaha Research, Auburn, NH, 2016).

_____, 2016b, *The Periodic Table of the 192 Quarks and Leptons in The Theory of Everything: The U(4) Layer Group, Physics is Logic VI* (Blaha Research, Auburn, NH, 2016).

_____, 2016c, *New Boson Quantum Field Theory, Dark Matter Dynamics, Dark Matter Fermion Layer Mixing, Genesis of Higgs Particles, New Layer Higgs Masses, Higgs Coupling Constants, Non-Abelian Higgs Gauge Fields, Physics is Logic VII* (Blaha Research, Auburn, NH, 2016).

_____, 2016d, *Unification of the Strong Interactions and Gravitation: Quark Confinement Linked to Modified Short-Distance Gravity; Physics is Logic VIII* (Blaha Research, Auburn, NH, 2016).

_____, 2016e, *MoND: Unification of the Strong Interactions and Gravitation II, Quark Confinement Linked to Large-Scale Gravity, Physics is Logic IX* (Blaha Research, Auburn, NH, 2016).

_____, 2016f, *CQ Mechanics: A Unification of Quantum & Classical Mechanics, Quantum/Semi-Classical Entanglement, Quantum/Classical Path Integrals, Quantum/Classical Chaos* (Blaha Research, Auburn, NH, 2016).

_____, 2016g, *GEMS Unified Gravity, ElectroMagnetic and Strong Interactions: Manifest Quark Confinement, A Solution for the Proton Spin Puzzle, Modified Gravity on the Galactic Scale* (Pingree Hill Publishing, Auburn, NH, 2016).

_____, 2016h, *Unification of the Seven Boson Interactions based on the Riemann-Christoffel Curvature Tensor* (Pingree Hill Publishing, Auburn, NH, 2016).

_____, 2017a, *Unification of the Eleven Boson Interactions based on 'Rotations of Interactions'* (Pingree Hill Publishing, Auburn, NH, 2017).

_____, 2017b, *The Origin of Fermions and Bosons, and Their Unification* (Pingree Hill Publishing, Auburn, NH, 2017).

_____, 2017c, *Megaverse: The Universe of Universes* (Pingree Hill Publishing, Auburn, NH, 2017).

_____, 2017d, *SuperSymmetry and the Unified SuperStandard Model* (Pingree Hill Publishing, Auburn, NH, 2017).

_____, 2017e, *From Qubits to the Unified SuperStandard Model with Embedded SuperStrings: A Derivation* (Pingree Hill Publishing, Auburn, NH, 2017).

_____, 2017f, *The Unified SuperStandard Model in Our Universe and the Megaverse: Quarks, ... ,* (Pingree Hill Publishing, Auburn, NH, 2017).

_____, 2018a, *The Unified SuperStandard Model and the Megaverse SECOND EDITION A Deeper Theory based on a New Particle Functional Space that Explicates Quantum Entanglement Spookiness (Volume 1)* (Pingree Hill Publishing, Auburn, NH, 2018).

_____, 2018b, *Cosmos Creation: The Unified SuperStandard Model, Volume 2, SECOND EDITION* (Pingree Hill Publishing, Auburn, NH, 2018).

_____, 2018c, *God Theory (*Pingree Hill Publishing, Auburn, NH, 2018).

_____, 2018d, *Immortal Eye: God Theory: Second Edition* (Pingree Hill Publishing, Auburn, NH, 2018).

_____, 2018e, *Unification of God Theory and Unified SuperStandard Model THIRD EDITION* (Pingree Hill Publishing, Auburn, NH, 2018).

_____, 2019a, *Calculation of: QED α = 1/137, and Other Coupling Constants of the Unified SuperStandard Theory* (Pingree Hill Publishing, Auburn, NH, 2019).

_____, 2019b, *Coupling Constants of the Unified SuperStandard Theory SECOND EDITION* (Pingree Hill Publishing, Auburn, NH, 2019).

_____, 2019c, *New Hybrid Quantum Big_Bang–Megaverse_Driven Universe with a Finite Big Bang and an Increasing Hubble Constant* (Pingree Hill Publishing, Auburn, NH, 2019).

_____, 2019d, *The Universe, The Electron and The Vacuum* (Pingree Hill Publishing, Auburn, NH, 2019).

_____, 2019e, *Quantum Big Bang – Quantum Vacuum Universes (Particles)* (Pingree Hill Publishing, Auburn, NH, 2019).

_____, 2019f, *The Exact QED Calculation of the Fine Structure Constant Implies ALL 4D Universes have the Same Physics/Life Prospects* (Pingree Hill Publishing, Auburn, NH, 2019).

_____, 2019g, *Unified SuperStandard Theory and the SuperUniverse Model: The Foundation of Science* (Pingree Hill Publishing, Auburn, NH, 2019).

_____, 2020a, *Quaternion Unified SuperStandard Theory (The QUeST) and Megaverse Octonion SuperStandard Theory (MOST)* (Pingree Hill Publishing, Auburn, NH, 2020).

_____, 2020b, *United Universes Quaternion Universe - Octonion Megaverse* (Pingree Hill Publishing, Auburn, NH, 2020).

_____, 2020c, *Unified SuperStandard Theories for Quaternion Universes & The Octonion Megaverse* (Pingree Hill Publishing, Auburn, NH, 2020).

_____, 2020d, *The Essence of Eternity: Quaternion & Octonion SuperStandard Theories* (Pingree Hill Publishing, Auburn, NH, 2020).

_____, 2020e, *The Essence of Eternity II* (Pingree Hill Publishing, Auburn, NH, 2020).

_____, 2020f, *A Very Conscious Universe* (Pingree Hill Publishing, Auburn, NH, 2020).

_____, 2020g, *Hypercomplex Universe* (Pingree Hill Publishing, Auburn, NH, 2020).

_____, 2020h, *Beneath the Quaternion Universe* (Pingree Hill Publishing, Auburn, NH, 2020).

_____, 2020i, *Why is the Universe Real? From Quaternion & Octonion to Real Coordinates* (Pingree Hill Publishing, Auburn, NH, 2020).

_____, 2020j, *The Origin of Universes: of Quaternion Unified SuperStandard Theory (QUeST); and of the Octonion Megaverse (UTMOST)* (Pingree Hill Publishing, Auburn, NH, 2020).

_____, 2020k, *The Seven Spaces of Creation: Octonion Cosmology* (Pingree Hill Publishing, Auburn, NH, 2020).

_____, 2020l, *From Octonion Cosmology to the Unified SuperStandard Theory of Particles* (Pingree Hill Publishing, Auburn, NH, 2020).

_____, 2021a, *Pioneering the Cosmos* (Pingree Hill Publishing, Auburn, NH, 2021).

_____, 2021b, *Pioneering the Cosmos II* (Pingree Hill Publishing, Auburn, NH, 2021).

_____, 2021c, *Beyond Octonion Cosmology* (Pingree Hill Publishing, Auburn, NH, 2021).

_____, 2021d, *Universes are Particles* (Pingree Hill Publishing, Auburn, NH, 2021).

_____, 2021e, *Octonion-like dna-based life, Universe expansion is decay, Emerging New Physics* (Pingree Hill Publishing, Auburn, NH, 2021).

_____, 2021f, *The Science of Creation New Quantum Field Theory of Spaces* (Pingree Hill Publishing, Auburn, NH, 2021).

_____, 2021g, *Quantum Space Theory With Application to Octonion Cosmology & Possibly To Fermionic Condensed Matter* (Pingree Hill Publishing, Auburn, NH, 2021).

_____, 2021h, *21st Century Natural Philosophy of Octonion Cosmology , and Predestination, Fate, and Free Will* (Pingree Hill Publishing, Auburn, NH, 2021).

_____, 2021i, *Beyond Octonion Cosmology II : Origin of the Quantum; A New Generalized Field Theory (GiFT); A Proof of the Spectrum of Universes; Atoms in Higher Universes* (Pingree Hill Publishing, Auburn, NH, 2021).

_____, 2021j, *Integration of General Relativity and Quantum Theory: Octonion Cosmology, GiFT, Creation/Annihilation Spaces CASe, Reduction of Spaces to a Few Fermions and Symmetries in Fundamental Frames* (Pingree Hill Publishing, Auburn, NH, 2021).

_____, 2022a, *New View of Octonion Cosmology Based on the Unification of General Relativit and Quantum Theory* (Pingree Hill Publishing, Auburn, NH, 2022).

_____, 2022b, *The Dust Beneath Hypercomplex Cosmology* (Pingree Hill Publishing, Auburn, NH, 2022).

_____, 2022c, *Passing Through Nature to Eternity: ProtoCosmos, HyperCosmos, Unified SuperStandard Theory* (Pingree Hill Publishing, Auburn, NH, 2022).

_____, 2022d, *HyperCosmos Fractionation and Fundamental Reference Frame Based Unification: Particle Inner Space Basis of Parton and Dual Resonance Models* (Pingree Hill Publishing, Auburn, NH, 2022).

_____, 2022e, *A New UniDimension ProtoCosmos and SuperString F-Theory Relation to the HyperCosmos* (Pingree Hill Publishing, Auburn, NH, 2022).

_____, 2022f, *The Cosmic Panorama: ProtoCosmos, HyperCosmos,Unified SuperStandard Theory (UST) Derivation* (Pingree Hill Publishing, Auburn, NH, 2022).

_____, 2022g, *Ultimate Origin: ProtoCosmos and HyperCosmos* (Pingree Hill Publishing, Auburn, NH, 2022).

_____, 2023a, *UltraUnification and the Generation of the Cosmos* (Pingree Hill Publishing, Auburn, NH, 2023).

_____, 2023b, *God and and Cosmos Theory* (Pingree Hill Publishing, Auburn, NH, 2023).

_____, 2023c, *A New Completely Geometric SU(8) Cosmos Theory; New PseudoFermion Fields; Fibonacci-like Dimension Arrays; Ramsey Number Approximation* (Pingree Hill Publishing, Auburn, NH, 2023).

_____, 2023d, *Newton's Apple is Now the Fermion* (Pingree Hill Publishing, Auburn, NH, 2023).

_____, 2023e, *Cosmos Theory: The Sub-Particle Gambol Model* (Pingree Hill Publishing, Auburn, NH, 2023).

_____, 2024a, *Cosmos-Universe-Particle-Gambol Theory* (Pingree Hill Publishing, Auburn, NH, 2024).

_____, 2024b, *Fractal Cosmos Theory* (Pingree Hill Publishing, Auburn, NH, 2024).

REFERENCES

_____, 2024c, *Fractal Cosmic Curve: Tensor-Based Cosmos Theory* (Pingree Hill Publishing, Auburn, NH, 2024).

Eddington, A. S., 1952, *The Mathematical Theory of Relativity* (Cambridge University Press, Cambridge, U.K., 1952).

Fant, Karl M., 2005, *Logically Determined Design: Clockless System Design With NULL Convention Logic* (John Wiley and Sons, Hoboken, NJ, 2005).

Feinberg, G. and Shapiro, R., 1980, *Life Beyond Earth: The Intelligent Earthlings Guide to Life in the Universe* (William Morrow and Company, New York, 1980).

Gelfand, I. M., Fomin, S. V., Silverman, R. A. (tr), 2000, *Calculus of Variations* (Dover Publications, Mineola, NY, 2000).

Giaquinta, M., Modica, G., Souchek, J., 1998, *Cartesian Coordinates in the Calculus of Variations* Volumes I and II (Springer-Verlag, New York, 1998).

Giaquinta, M., Hildebrandt, S., 1996, *Calculus of Variations* Volumes I and II (Springer-Verlag, New York, 1996).

Gradshteyn, I. S. and Ryzhik, I. M., 1965, *Table of Integrals, Series, and Products* (Academic Press, New York, 1965).

Heitler, W., 1954, *The Quantum Theory of Radiation* (Claendon Press, Oxford, UK, 1954).

Huang, Kerson, 1992, *Quarks, Leptons & Gauge Fields 2nd Edition* (World Scientific Publishing Company, Singapore, 1992).

Jost, J., Li-Jost, X., 1998, *Calculus of Variations* (Cambridge University Press, New York, 1998).

Kaku, Michio, 1993, *Quantum Field Theory*, (Oxford University Press, New York, 1993).

Kirk, G. S. and Raven, J. E., 1962, *The Presocratic Philosophers* (Cambridge University Press, New York, 1962).

Landau, L. D. and Lifshitz, E. M., 1987, *Fluid Mechanics 2nd Edition*, (Pergamon Press, Elmsford, NY, 1987).

Misner, C. W., Thorne, K. S., and Wheeler, J. A., 1973, *Gravitation* (W. H. Freeman, New York, 1973).

Rescher, N., 1967, *The Philosophy of Leibniz* (Prentice-Hall, Englewood Cliffs, NJ, 1967).

Rieffel, Eleanor and Polak, Wolfgang, 2014, *Quantum Computing* (MIT Press, Cambridge, MA, 2014).

Riesz, Frigyes and Sz.-Nagy, Béla, 1990, *Functional Analysis* (Dover Publications, New York, 1990).

Sagan, H., 1993, *Introduction to the Calculus of Variations* (Dover Publications, Mineola, NY, 1993).

Sakurai, J. J., 1964, *Invariance Principles and Elementary Particles* (Princeton University Press, Princeton, NJ, 1964).

Weinberg, S., 1972, *Gravitation and Cosmology* (John Wiley and Sons, New York, 1972).

Weinberg, S., 1995, *The Quantum Theory of Fields Volume I* (Cambridge University Press, New York, 1995).

INDEX

About the Author

Stephen Blaha is a well-known Physicist and Man of Letters with interests in Science, Society and civilization, the Arts, and Technology. He had an Alfred P. Sloan Foundation scholarship in college. He received his Ph.D. in Physics from Rockefeller University. He has served on the faculties of several major universities. He was also a Member of the Technical Staff at Bell Laboratories, a manager at the Boston Globe Newspaper, a Director at Wang Laboratories, and President of Blaha Software Inc. and of Janus Associates Inc. (NH).

Among other achievements he was a co-discoverer of the "r potential" for heavy quark binding developing the first (and still the only demonstrable) non-Aeolian gauge theory with an "r" potential; first suggested the existence of topological structures in superfluid He-3; first proposed Yang-Mills theories would appear in condensed matter phenomena with non-scalar order parameters; first developed a grammar-based formalism for quantum computers and applied it to elementary particle theories; first developed a new form of quantum field theory without divergences (thus solving a major 60 year old problem that enabled a unified theory of the Standard Model and Quantum Gravity without divergences to be developed); first developed a formulation of complex General Relativity based on analytic continuation from real space-time; first developed a generalized non-homogeneous Robertson-Walker metric that enabled a quantum theory of the Big Bang to be developed without singularities at t = 0; first generalized Cauchy's theorem and Gauss' theorem to complex, curved multi-dimensional spaces; received Honorable Mention in the Gravity Research Foundation Essay Competition in 1978; first developed a physically acceptable theory of faster-than-light particles; first derived a composition of extremums method in the Calculus of Variations; first quantitatively suggested that inflationary periods in the history of the universe were not needed; first proved Gödel's Theorem implies Nature must be quantum; provided a new alternative to the Higgs Mechanism, and Higgs particles, to generate masses; first showed how to resolve logical paradoxes including Gödel's Undecidability Theorem by developing Operator Logic and Quantum Operator Logic; first developed a quantitative harmonic oscillator-like model of the life cycle, and interactions, of civilizations; first showed how equations describing superorganisms also apply to civilizations. A recent book shows his theory applies successfully to the past 14 years of history and to *new* archaeological data on Andean and Mayan civilizations as well as Early Anatolian and Egyptian civilizations.

He first developed an axiomatic derivation of the form of The Standard Model from geometry – space-time properties – The Unified SuperStandard Model. It unifies all the known forces of Nature. It also has a Dark Matter sector that includes a Dark ElectroWeak sector with Dark doublets and Dark gauge interactions. It uses quantum coordinates to remove infinities that crop up in most interacting quantum field theories and additionally to remove the infinities that appear in the Big Bang and generate inflationary growth of the universe. It shows gravity has a MOND-like form without sacrificing Newton's Laws. It relates the interactions of the MOND-like sector of gravity with the r-potential of Quark Confinement. The axioms of the theory lead to the question of their origin. We suggest in the preceding edition of this book it can be attributed to an entity with God-like properties. We explore these properties in "God Theory" and show they predict that the Cosmos exists forever although individual universes (or incarnations of our universe) "come and go." Several other important results emerge from God Theory such a functionally triune God. The Unified SuperStandard Theory has many other important parts described in the Current Edition of *The Unified SuperStandard Theory* and expanded in subsequent volumes.

Blaha has had a major impact on a succession of elementary particle theories: his Ph.D. thesis (1970), and papers, showed that quantum field theory calculations to all orders in ladder approximations could not give scaling deep inelastic electron-nucleon scattering. He later showed the eigenvalue equation for the fine structure constant α in Johnson-Baker-Willey QED had a zero at $\alpha = 1$ not 1/137 by solving the Schwinger-Dyson equations to all orders in an approximation that agreed with exact results to 4th order in α thus ending interest in this theory. In 1979 at Prof. Ken Johnson's (MIT) suggestion he calculated the proton-neutron mass difference in the MIT bag model and found the result had the wrong sign reducing interest in the bag model. These results all appear in Physical Review papers. In the 2000's he repeatedly pointed out the shortcomings of SuperString theory and showed that The Standard Model's form could be derived from space-time geometry by an extension of Lorentz transformations to faster than light transformations. This deeper space-time basis greatly increases the possibility that it is part of THE fundamental theory. Recently, Blaha showed that the Weak interactions differed significantly from the Strong, electromagnetic and gravitation interactions in important respects while these interactions had similar features, and suggested that ElectroWeak theory, which is essentially a glued union of the Weak interactions and Electromagnetism, possibly modulo unknown Higgs particle features, be replaced by a unified theory of the other interactions combined with a stand-alone Weak interaction theory. Blaha also showed that, if Charmonium calculations are taken seriously, the Strong interaction coupling constant is only a factor of five larger than the electromagnetic coupling constant, and thus Strong interaction perturbation theory would make sense and yield physically meaningful results.

In graduate school (1965-71) he wrote substantial papers in elementary particles and group theory: The Inelastic E- P Structure Functions in a Gluon Model. Phys. Lett. B40:501-502,1972; Deep-Inelastic E-P Structure Functions In A Ladder Model With Spin 1/2 Nucleons, Phys.Rev. D3:510-523,1971; Continuum Contributions To The Pion Radius, Phys. Rev. 178:2167-2169,1969; Character Analysis of U(N) and SU(N), J. Math. Phys. 10, 2156 (1969); and The Calculation of the Irreducible Characters of the Symmetric Group in Terms of the Compound Characters, (Published as Blaha's Lemma in D. E. Knuth's book: *The Art of Computer Programming Vols. 1 – 4*).

In the early 1980's Blaha was also a pioneer in the development of UNIX for financial, scientific and Internet applications: benchmarked UNIX versions showing that block size was critical for UNIX performance, developing financial modeling software, starting database benchmarking comparison studies, developing Internet-like UNIX networking (1982) and developing a hybrid shell programming technique (1982) that was a precursor to the PERL programming language. He was also the manager of the AT&T ten-year future products development database. His work helped lead to commercial UNIX on computers such as Sun Micros, IBM AIX minis, and Apple computers.

In the 1980's he pioneered the development of PC Desktop Publishing on laser printers and was nominated for three "Awards for Technical Excellence" in 1987 by PC Magazine for PC software products that he designed and developed.

Recently he has developed a theory of Megaverses – actual universes of which our universe is one – with quantum particle-like properties based on the Wheeler-DeWitt equation of Quantum Gravity. He has developed a theory of a baryonic force, which had been conjectured many years ago, and estimated the strength of the force based on discrepancies in measurements of the gravitational constant G. This force, operative in D-dimensional space, can be used to escape from our universe in "uniships" which are the equivalent of the faster-than-light starships proposed in the author's earlier books. Thus travel to other universes, as well as to other stars is possible.

Blaha also considered the complexified Wheeler-DeWitt equation and showed that its limitation to real-valued coordinates and metrics generated a Cosmological Constant in the Einstein equations.

The author has also recently written a series of books on the serious problems of the United States and their solution as well as a book on the decline of Mankind that will follow from current social and genetic trends in Mankind.

In the past twenty years Dr. Blaha has written over 80 books on a wide range of topics. Some recent major works are: *From Asynchronous Logic to The Standard Model to Superflight to the Stars, All the Universe!, SuperCivilizations: Civilizations as Superorganisms, America's Future: an Islamic Surge, ISIS, al Qaeda, World Epidemics, Ukraine, Russia-China Pact, US Leadership Crisis, The Rises and Falls of Man – Destiny – 3000 AD: New Support for a Superorganism MACRO-THEORY of CIVILIZATIONS From CURRENT WORLD TRENDS and NEW Peruvian, Pre-Mayan, Mayan, Anatolian, and Early Egyptian Data, with a Projection to 3000 AD,* and *Mankind in Decline: Genetic Disasters, Human-Animal Hybrids, Overpopulation, Pollution, Global Warming, Food and Water Shortages, Desertification, Poverty, Rising Violence, Genocide, Epidemics, Wars, Leadership Failure.*

He has taught approximately 4,000 students in undergraduate, graduate, and postgraduate corporate education courses primarily in major universities, and large companies and government agencies.

He developed a quantum theory, The Unified SuperStandard Theory (UST), which describes elementary particles in detail without the difficulties of conventional quantum field theory. He found that the internal symmetries of this theory could be exactly derived from an octonion theory called QUeST. He further found that another octonion theory (UTMOST) describes the Megaverse. It can hold QUeST universes such as our own universe. It has an internal symmetry structure which is a superset of the QUeST internal symmetries.

Recently he developed Octonion Cosmology. He replaced it with HyperCosmos theory, which has significantly better features. He developed a fractionalization process for dimensions, particles and symmetry groups. He also described transformation that reduced particles and dimensions to a far more compact form. He also developed a precursor theory ProtoCosmos that leads to the HyperCosmos.

The author showed that space-time and Internal Symmetries can be unified in any of the ten HyperCosmos spaces in their associated HyperUnification spaces. The combined set of HyperUnification spaces enable all HyperCosmos dimensions to be obtained by a General Relativistic transformation from one primordial dimension in the 42 space-time dimension unified HyperUnification space.

At present the author devel;oped the Cosmos Theory that incorporates ProtoCosmos Theory, HyperCosmos Theory, Limos Theory, Second Kind HyperCosmos Theory and HyperUnification Spaces. He has introduced PseudoFermion wave functions and theory, He has related Cosmos Theory to Regge trajectories of spaces, parton theory, Veneziano amplitudes, Fibonacci numbers and Ramsey numbers. He has calculated an approximation to the difficult R(n,n) Ramsey numbers.

He has developed a Gambol Model that successfully accounts for e-p deep inelastic scattering, fundamental particle resonances, hadron scattering, and the inner structure of particles based on confinement through Casimir forces of ideal gambol gases. The Gambol Planckian Distribution was derived.

He has applied the Gambol Model to particles, universes, and the Cosmos of universes. He showed that the Cosmos may have a distribution of 23 universes corresponding to various Cosmos spaces.

Recently he showed that Cosmos Theory follows from the number of independent asymmetric tensors in a dimension r. He also showed the close parallel between the form of γ-matrices and Cosmos Theory dimension arrays.